CAPS, COMMAS, AND OTHER THINGS

Developing Skills in English/ Grades 2-8 and Remedial

CAPS, COMMAS, AND OTHER THINGS

Developing Skills in English/ Grades 2-8 and Remedial

Sheryl Pastorek

Academic Therapy Publications
Novato, California

Academic Therapy Publications, 20 Commercial Boulevard, Novato, CA 94949-6191

International Standard Book Number: 0-87879-325-9

2 1 0 9 8 7 6 5 4 3
4 3 2 1 0 9 8 7 6 5

INTRODUCTION

Teachers in regular and special settings, grades 3 through 8, and in upper level remedial settings, find themselves faced with a broad range of student abilities in English skills. They have long searched for and frequently requested a source that offers flexibility and a wide variety of levels in English.

Caps, Commas, and Other Things is the answer to this need. Not only does it provide a broad range, but also a considerable monetary saving to the teacher because all materials in this manual may be freely copied for either individual or class use (as long as the material is not sold). In addition, because of the wide use of the *Test of Written English* (Academic Therapy Publications, 1979, Andersen and Thompson), this manual of practical activities may be used either as a follow-up to that assesment or on its own. In other words, use the material in sequence or use what you need as you need it.

Levels in *Caps, Commas, and Other Things* closely parallel the graded skills given in the *Test of Written English* (TWE). Written language skills are covered in two main sections — Capitalization/Punctuation and Written Expression. There are six levels in the Capitalization/Punctuation section and four levels in the Written Expression section.

Each Overview section provides the teacher with the sequence for the worksheets, activities, et cetera for the Capitalization/Punctuation and Written Expression sections. Each Overview has been designed for developing instructional objectives and lesson plans from its contents. Here, again, the teacher can use all of the activities and worksheets in each section to teach or review the skills covered with students or can use only those items needed to remediate a student's specific deficit skills.

While the material is arranged sequentially, you may start wherever the needs of your students dictate. For example, if tests and/or observations indicate that capitalization of the first word in a sentence is not a problem (Section I, Level One), then move right into capitalization of proper names (Section I, Level Two).

Use of Caps, Commas, and Other things

While some school districts allow the staff to use the school photocopier, others do not. Therefore, the book has been designed so that worksheets can be duplicated .

★   ★   ★

Caps, Commas, and Other Things provides an effective tool for the development and remediation of written language skills. It has been designed with classroom and special education teachers in mind. Classroom teachers may find the material useful with large groups, small groups, or on an individual basis. The worksheets and activities can be used for actual instruction of skills or for review and practice of specific skills. Special education teachers may want to use the worksheets and activities for remediation of deficit skills. Lesson plans and instructional objectives can be easily formulated from the contents of the book. It is recommended that other written language materials (either teacher-made or published) be utilized in conjunction with this book. *Caps, Commas, and Other Things* can be used as a supplement to these materials or vice versa.

TABLE OF CONTENTS

SECTION II – WRITTEN EXPRESSION

OVERVIEW

A. **CAPITALIZATION** — First word of a sentence; Pronoun "I"

1. **Introduction:** Put sentences on the chalkboard with capital letters in a different color chalk. Discuss the need for capital letters at the beginning of sentences. Students are to copy the sentences onto their papers.

   Sentences:
   a. We are going to visit the zoo.
   b. I like to read books.
   c. The postman brings our mail.
   d. My father and I went to the ball game.
   e. These are the books that I lost.
   f. They went to the beach for a vacation.
   g. I bought some new clothes.
   h. The teacher took her class on a walking trip.

2. Worksheet #1

3. **Boardwork** — Write sentences on the chalkboard with small letters. Students are to copy the sentences and are to put in the missing capital letters.

   Sentences:
   a. the children are playing in the backyard.
   b. we learned to play a new game.
   c. the music is too loud.
   d. the men are painting our house.
   e. i have to go to the store.
   f. my mother and i are baking cookies.
   g. the women are sewing a quilt.
   h. that chair is broken.

4. Worksheet #2

5. Worksheet #3

6. Worksheet #4

7. Worksheet #5 — TEST

B. **PUNCTUATION** — Period at the end of the sentence; question mark at the end of the sentence.

   1. **Introduction:** Write sentences on the chalkboard. Use a different color chalk to put in the period. Students are to copy the sentences (statements).

      Sentences:

      a. Today is a nice day.

      b. We are in school now.

      c. I have some new pencils.

      d. The new books have come in.

      e. We have a nice library at our school.

      f. He has a new red bike.

      g. I forgot to mail the letters.

      h. It is time to go to school.

   2. Worksheet #6

   3. Worksheet #7

   4. **Introduction:** Write questions on the chalkboard. Use a different color chalk to put in the question mark. Students are to copy the questions onto their papers.

      Sentences:

      a. Where do you live?

      b. Do you have an extra pencil?

      c. Which bicycle belongs to you?

      d. What time is the party?

      e. Can you run fast?

      f. Do you like math?

      g. May we go play baseball now?

      h. Is this your blue sweater?

   5. Worksheet #8

   6. Worksheet #9

   7. **Boardwork** — Copy these sentences. Put in the missing period or question mark.

Sentences:

a. We need to go to school to learn

b. What are you doing

c. Are you going to the party

d. It has been raining hard

e. May we have some cheese and crackers

f. The boys are playing football today

g. Where did you put my blue sweater

h. How fast can you run

i. Which book do you want

j. The girls have gone shopping

8. Worksheet #10

9. Worksheet #11

10. Worksheet #12 – TEST

C. REVIEW

1. **Boardwork** – Read each sentence. Copy each sentence putting in the needed capital letters and punctuation marks.

    Sentences:

    a. we are going to do our homework now

    b. are you going to the party

    c. mother and i are fixing supper

    d. the dog is chasing the cat down the street

    e. what is your favorite fruit

    f. today i have to go to the dentist

    g. he is a good soccer player

    h. this is our new house

    i. will you help me lift this box

    j. i want to get a new bike

    k. everybody has finished his work

    l. how soon will we eat dinner

2. Worksheet #13

3. Worksheet #14 – TEST

NAME_____ DATE_____

Read each sentence. Circle the words that should be capitalized. Write the correct capital letter above each circled word. The first one has been done for you.

1. (the) store is not open today.

2. jane has a new dress on today.

3. my mother and i baked a cake.

4. may i go to the party this Saturday?

5. where is the fire?

6. i need to get a book from the library.

7. how far is it to your school?

8. bob went to play ball with his friends.

9. can you come over to my house for supper?

10. my father said that i have to stay home.

11. mrs. Brown lives next door to us.

12. we are going to the beach to swim and to have a picnic.

13. easter is a special time of year.

14. mr. and Mrs. Jones have gone to the mountains on vacation.

15. the teacher took her class to visit the museum.

NAME_____ DATE_____

Read the sentences. Rewrite the sentences in correct form on the line below each printed sentence. The first one has been done for you.

1. John Went To The Park To Play.

   John went to the park to play.

2. My Mother Has Gone To The Store.

   _____

3. Where Did You Put Your Books?

   _____

4. I Need To Get A New Car.

   _____

5. My Sister Is Going To Visit Her Friend.

   _____

6. How Old Are You?

   _____

7. Bill And I Are Playing Ball This Afternoon.

   _____

8. What Time Does The Show Begin?

   _____

9. Which One Of You Broke The Window?

   _____

10. Where Does That Man Live?

   _____

NAME_____ DATE_____

Read each sentence in Part A. Copy the capital letters into the appropriate blanks in Part B. The first one has been done for you.

PART A

1. We went to our grandparent's house for dinner.

2. Can you help me with my homework?

3. Bob and I are going to ride our bikes after school.

4. Where did you put your sweater?

5. The man had a big smile on his face.

6. Christmas is my favorite holiday.

7. What can I do to help you?

8. The teacher gave us a lot of homework.

9. I have to go to the doctor's tomorrow.

10. Will you play checkers with me?

PART B

1. We went to our grandparent's house for dinner.

2. ___an you help me with my homework?

3. ___ob and ___ are going to ride our bikes after school.

4. ___here did you put your sweater?

5. ___he man had a big smile on his face.

6. ___hristmas is my favorite holiday.

7. ___hat can ___ do to help you?

8. ___he teacher gave us a lot of homework.

9. ___ have to go to the doctor's tomorrow.

10. ___ill you play checkers with me?

CAPITALIZATION/PUNCTUATION WS#4

NAME_____ DATE_____

Read each sentence. Write the sentence in correct form on the line below the printed sentence. The first one has been done for you.

1. may i go and play at Tom's house?

   May I go and play at Tom's house?

2. our teacher is not here today.

   _____

3. when are we going to the store?

   _____

4. it is a cloudy day.

   _____

5. the wind is blowing hard..

   _____

6. it looks like it is going to rain.

   _____

7. mother and i are making cookies.

   _____

8. may i have another apple?

   _____

9. where did you find this book?

   _____

10. the teacher said that i may read now.

    _____

16

NAME_____ DATE_____

TEST

Read each sentence. Write only those sentences which need corrections on the lines below each printed sentence.

1. there are no cookies left.

   _____

2. Mother and i cleaned the whole house.

   _____

3. The teacher was very happy with our work.

   _____

4. Did you finish all of your homework?

   _____

5. what is your favorite holiday?

   _____

6. may i spend the night at Jane's house?

   _____

7. i cannot run as fast as you.

   _____

8. Have you seen our new car?

   _____

9. when do you have to go home?

   _____

10. We went out to eat dinner.

    _____

11. mrs. Greensmith is a nice lady.

    _____

12. My friend and i have fun playing ball.

    _____

13. tom hit a home run.

    _____

14. It is supposed to be a sunny day.

    _____

15. all of the children enjoyed seeing the play.

    _____

NAME_____ DATE_____

Put the correct punctuation mark at the end of each sentence.

1. We are going swimming

2. I have to go home now

3. Please sit down and do your work

4. Our television is not working

5. She is not doing her homework

6. They bought a new home

7. My parents have gone on a trip

8. It will rain soon

9. We had fresh orange juice to drink

10. The boys have gone to see a movie

11. The chair is broken

12. My mother got a new job

13. The leaves are falling off the trees

14. Tom and Karen are playing chess

15. There are some pretty flowers out in the garden

NAME _____ DATE_____

Read each sentence (statement). Write the sentence on the line and put in the missing punctuation mark.

1. Today is John's birthday

_____

2. We are going to his birthday party

_____

3. There will be cake and ice cream to eat

_____

4. There will be games to play

_____

5. We may win some prizes

_____

6. John will get birthday gifts

_____

7. We should have fun at the party

_____

8. We will stay for two hours

_____

9. Then it will be time to go home

_____

10. We like to go to birthday parties

_____

NAME_____ DATE_____

Read each sentence. Put in the missing punctuation marks.

1. When do you have to go home

2. Do you like to play soccer

3. Have you seen my new bike

4. Will you help me with my homework

5. What is your favorite game to play

6. Are you feeling any better today

7. Did you find your spelling book

8. Did the lunch bell ring yet

9. Where are the wooden rulers

10. Do you need any more glue

11. Who lost the ball

12. Whose pencil is this

13. Would you please be quiet

14. Did you close the door

15. Is it still snowing

NAME_____ DATE_____

Read each sentence. Put in the missing punctuation marks. Write your answer on the line.

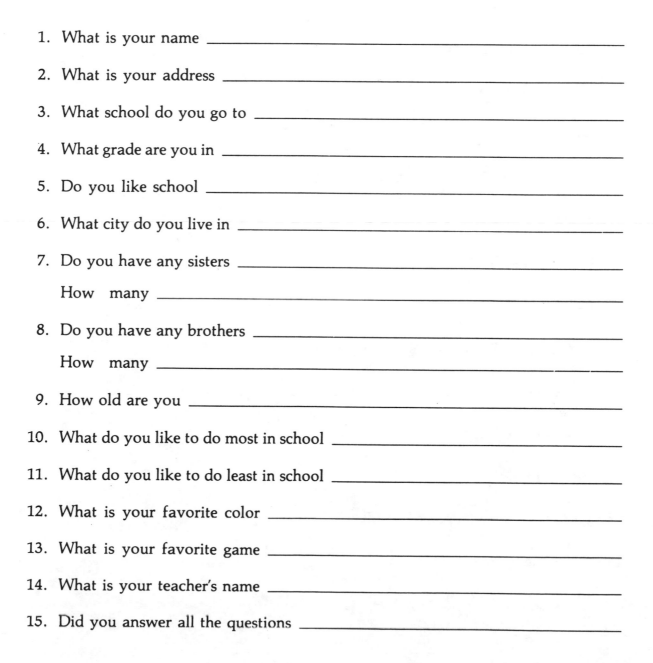

1. What is your name _____

2. What is your address _____

3. What school do you go to _____

4. What grade are you in _____

5. Do you like school _____

6. What city do you live in _____

7. Do you have any sisters _____

   How many _____

8. Do you have any brothers _____

   How many _____

9. How old are you _____

10. What do you like to do most in school _____

11. What do you like to do least in school _____

12. What is your favorite color _____

13. What is your favorite game _____

14. What is your teacher's name _____

15. Did you answer all the questions _____

NAME_____ DATE_____

Read each sentence. Put in the missing period or question mark.

1. When is it time for lunch

2. Lunch is at twelve o'clock

3. What are we having for dinner

4. We are having hamburgers, corn, and french fries

5. There is a new boy in our room

6. What is his name

7. His name is Carl

8. Did you mow the grass

9. I am almost finished with the mowing

10. There are no cookies left in the jar

11. Who ate the last one

12. I don't know

13. Our team played a game last night

14. Did your team win the game

15. No, we lost the game by two points

NAME_____ DATE_____

Read each sentence. Some of the sentences are punctuated correctly and some are punctuated incorrectly. Rewrite the incorrect sentences and put in the correct punctuation mark.

1. Where did you get that?

   _____

2. The dog is barking loudly?

   _____

3. Why are you running so fast.

   _____

4. We had fun watching the monkeys at the zoo.

   _____

5. May we go and play at the park?

   _____

6. She got a new dress for her birthday?

   _____

7. Have you mowed the lawn.

   _____

8. Our neighbors are moving away?

   _____

9. Will you please put your things away?

   _____

10. This is an interesting book to read.

   _____

11. Mary and Susan are studying for the test?

   _____

12. We went to visit our grandparents yesterday?

   _____

NAME_____ DATE_____

TEST

Read each sentence and punctuate it correctly.

1. How many people are coming to the party

2. Where does your father work

3. Our house is being painted

4. The mother cat is taking good care of her kittens

5. The clock is chiming the hour

6. What happened at the car race

7. Who left the bike in the driveway

8. Have you finished all of your homework

9. The policeman helped us cross the busy street

10. What did you eat for breakfast

11. The tall man walked very quickly

12. Is Tom going to play ball

13. The girls went to see a funny movie

14. Do you know how to play the piano

15. There are pretty flowers in our garden

CAPITALIZATION/PUNCTUATION

NAME_____ DATE_____

Read each sentence. Write each sentence in correct form on the line below each printed sentence. Put in the missing capital letters and punctuation marks. The first one has been done for you.

1. i have to stay after school

   I have to stay after school.

2. what time do you have to be home

   _____

3. we have had sunny days this week

   _____

4. where did you put my jacket

   _____

5. when are you going on vacation

   _____

6. last week it rained on several days

   _____

7. our class is going to visit a farm

   _____

8. my grandparents are coming for a visit

   _____

9. where do i catch the school bus

   _____

10. may we go see a movie

   _____

11. there is a pretty rainbow in the sky

   _____

12. have you found your lost keys

   _____

NAME_____ DATE_____

TEST

Read each sentence. Write each sentence in correct form on the line below each printed sentence. Put in the missing capital letters and punctuation marks. The first one has been done for you.

1. what time is it

   What time is it?

2. the sun is shining today

   _____

3. i have a new puppy named Lucky

   _____

4. we are having a test tomorrow

   _____

5. when do i have to do my book report

   _____

6. will you help me plant the garden

   _____

7. the rabbit got stuck in the fence

   _____

8. would you come to our house for dinner

   _____

9. mother is making a cake

   _____

10. where did i put my lunch

    _____

11. we went to the basketball game

    _____

12. who put gum on the chair

    _____

OVERVIEW

A. **CAPITALIZATION**—Proper nouns (names of people and pets, months, days, holidays).

   1. **Introduction**—Put sentences on the chalkboard with the capital letters for people's and pet's names in a different color chalk. Students copy sentences after discussion.

      Sentences:
      a. His name is Joseph.
      b. The dog's name is Spot.
      c. Her name is Sally.
      d. Bill has a cat named Tiger.
      e. Paul Smith is a new boy at our school.
      f. Where have Marie and Susan gone?
      g. Rover is a name for a dog.
      h. We saw Les and Mike at the carnival.

   2. Worksheet #15

   3. **Boardwork**—Write at least ten names (first and last) on the chalkboard—use names of students in your room. Use all lower case letters. Have the students copy them onto paper putting in the needed capital letters.

      example: ellen jones

   4. **Activity/Bulletin Board**—Give each student a rectangular piece of white construction paper. Have them write their first and last name on it. Put both capital letters in a different color. Put these up on a bulletin board. Title it at the top "OUR CLASSROOM." At the bottom, put this rule — "We begin people's names with CAPITAL letters."

   5. Worksheet #16

   6. **Boardwork**—Write the days of the week on the chalkboard with capital letters in a different color chalk. Students are to copy the days onto their papers.

Monday	Friday
Tuesday	Saturday
Wednesday	Sunday
Thursday	

7.   Worksheet #17

8.   Worksheet #18

9.   **Activity** — Make a chart or mobile with the days of the week. Put the capital letter for each in a different color and underline the capital letter, too.

10. **Boardwork** — Write the months of the year on the chalkboard with the capital letter in a different color chalk. Students are to copy the months onto their papers.

January	May	September
February	June	October
March	July	November
April	August	December

11. Worksheet #19

12. **Activity** — Make a chart or mobile for the months of the year. Put the capital letters in a different color and underline the capital letter, too.

13. **Activity/Interest Center** — days of the week; months of the year. Put the days and months on separate cards with the capital letters in a different color ink. The days should be put in a mixed order in one envelope and the months should be put in a mixed order in another envelope. Make a worksheet for days and months. List the numbers 1 - 7 for the days and the numbers 1 - 12 for the months on the worksheet. The students should take turns putting the worksheet in the correct order. The teacher should check their answers.

14. **Boardwork** — Write the holidays on the chalkboard with the capital letters in a different color chalk. Students are to copy the holidays onto their papers after discussion is completed.

Christmas	New Year's Eve	Flag Day
Thanksgiving	Christmas Eve	Fourth of July
Halloween	Valentine's Day	April Fools' Day
Easter	May Day	St. Patrick's Day
New Year's Day	Mother's Day	President's Day
Palm Sunday	Father's Day	Veteran's Day
Memorial Day	Labor Day	Hanukkah

15. Worksheet #20

16. Worksheet #21

17. Worksheet #22

18. Worksheet #23

19. **Boardwork** — Copy the sentences from the chalkboard. Correct the errors.

Sentences:

a. Our neighbors are going to the lake for a vacation in july.

b. She is going to the dentist on tuesday.

c. We will begin school in september.

d. Who is going to the library on thursday?

e. We celebrate halloween in october.

f. new year's eve and new year's day are the start of a new year.

g. The boys are going to play ball on friday and saturday.

h. What time is the meeting on monday?

i. Our family is going away for christmas.

j. It is hot in august.

20. Worksheet #24

21. Worksheet #25 — Review Test

B. **CAPITALIZATION** — Initials and Abbreviations (i.e., Mr. Mrs.)

1. **Introduction** — Write sentences on the chalkboard with capital letters for this rule in a different color chalk. Students are to copy sentences onto their paper after discussion of each abbreviation.

Sentences:

a. Mr. Jones is a nice man.

b. What time is Miss Johnson coming?

c. Have you gone to see Dr. Carson?

d. Mrs. Lewis is baking a cake.

e. His name is J. H. Robinson.

f. Her initials are K. L. T.

g. I met Ms. R. Randall.

2. Worksheet #26

3. **Activity** — Give the students an old workbook, magazine, or newspaper page. Have them read through the page and circle the capital letters that apply to the rules studied. They should use a different color for each of the rules — Set 1 (proper names, pets, names, days, holidays, months); Set 2 (first word of sentence, "I," initials, abbreviations).

4. **Boardwork** — Write the names of the teachers in your school on the chalkboard. Put *Mr., Mrs., Miss, Ms.*, with the capital letter in a different color chalk. Have students copy these names onto their papers.

5. Worksheet #27

6. Worksheet #28 — TEST

C. **PUNCTUATION — Comma in dates**

1. **Introduction** — Put today's date on the chalkboard with the comma missing. Add the comma in a different color chalk. Then, ask the students to give you their birthdates. Put several of the dates on the chalkboard and have the students come up and put in the needed commas. Students are to copy these dates onto their papers.

2. **Boardwork** — Put sentences on the chalkboard with the comma between the date in a different color chalk. Students are to copy the sentences onto their papers.

   Sentences:

   a. Today is _____ ____, _____.
   b. Bob's birthdate is May 15, 1970.
   c. We went to the museum on October 16, 1980.
   d. Mrs. Cook had a baby girl on September 11, 1979.
   e. My parents were married on December 29, 1949.
   f. Our neighbors went to Hawaii on February 16, 1980.
   g. Tomorrow will be _____ ____, _____.
   h. We went to see the high school play on May 6, 1980.

3. Worksheet #29

D. **PUNCTUATION — Period in abbreviations and initials.**

1. **Introduction** — Put various abbreviations on the chalkboard and put the period in a different color chalk (e.g., Miss, Mr., Mrs., Rev., Dr., Ms.); put some of the students' initials on the chalkboard and put the periods in a different color chalk (e.g., K. M. Smith, L. V. Watson). Have the students copy these onto their papers after discussion.

2. **Boardwork** — Read each sentence. Put in the missing punctuation marks.

   Sentences:

   a. We met Mr and Mrs Walker at the concert.
   b. Mother went to see Dr Johnson.
   c. My friend's name is P S Thomas.
   d. His name is Andy S Rowland.
   e. Our teacher's name is Miss Jackson.

      f. Mr Robinson, Mr Samuels, Dr Cook and Rev Kirk are playing tennis.

      g. Mr and Mrs Anderson went to visit the new neighbors.

      h. Rev Barnett is our new minister.

      i. Her initials are Ms B G Somers.

      j. Our friends invited Rev and Mrs R Cooper over for dinner.

3.   Worksheet #30

4.   Worksheet #31

5.   Worksheet #32 — TEST

6.   **Bulletin Board** — INITIALS & ABBREVIATIONS(Title)

Give each student a white rectangular piece of construction paper. Have the students put their initials on it (i.e., S. J. Moore or Sally J. Moore or S. J. M.). Put these up on one side of the board (under the INITIALS side). Then put up the teachers' names in your school on the other side of the board utilizing Mr., Mrs., Miss and Ms. (if possible).

E. REVIEW

1.   **Boardwork** — Read each sentence. Copy each sentence putting in the missing capital letters and punctuation marks.

    Sentences:

    a. The new pastor is rev richard johnson.

    b. Today is _____ _____ _____.

    c. It is colder in december and january.

    d. I like the holiday of christmas.

    e. mr and mrs taylor have moved to a new house.

    f. miss mary l brown is the school nurse.

    g. What time does sam have to come home?

    h. My cat, tabby, is going to have kittens.

    i. The holiday that comes in october is halloween.

    j. Is Grandmother Carlson coming to visit us on wednesday or thursday?

2.   Worksheet #33

3.   Worksheet #34

4.   Worksheet #35

5.   Worksheet #36

6. Worksheet #37

7. Worksheet #38—TEST

NAME_____ DATE_____

Read each sentence. Circle the words that need capital letters. Write the correct capital letter above the circled word. The first one has been done for you.

1. He named his new cat *T*abby.

2. That bike belongs to bobby.

3. mary, beth, jane, and karen are playing a new game.

4. Have you seen my cat fluffy?

5. They have gone to visit bill and marie.

6. Our dog, rover, is fun to play with all the time.

7. I saw scott, tony, and sandy at the ball game.

8. What time are you going to visit john?

9. My horse, flicka, ran a fast race.

10. My best friends are joan and sarah.

11. My sister's name is janice.

12. They named the new baby girl jennifer.

13. The parrot's name is polly.

14. marmaduke is the name of a dog in the cartoons.

15. My father's name is john.

NAME_____ DATE_____

Read each sentence. Circle each word that needs a capital letter. Rewrite the sentence putting in the needed capital letters. The first one has been done for you.

1. His dog is named (max)

   His dog is named Max.

2. I saw jack at the zoo.

   _____

3. Have you read the story about the horse, black beauty?

   _____

4. beth and carol are not here now.

   _____

5. Their horse, charger, can run very fast.

   _____

6. My cat, patches, is going to have kittens.

   _____

7. george is a funny name for a monkey.

   _____

8. My best friend is ken brown.

   _____

9. Her name is mary turner.

   _____

10. We saw bob cooper and bob smith at the parade.

    _____

NAME_____ DATE_____

PART A: Read each sentence. Circle the letters that should be capitals and write the capital letters above.

1. There is no school on saturday and sunday.

2. We are going to play tennis on wednesday.

3. Our class is going to the science museum on friday.

4. His birthday is next monday.

5. Can you come over to my house on thursday?

6. Father and Mother are going out to dinner on tuesday.

PART B: Write a sentence for each word below.

1. Thursday

_____

2. Sunday

_____

3. Wednesday

_____

4. Monday

_____

5. Friday

_____

NAME _____ DATE_____

Read each sentence. The underlined word is capitalized for one of three reasons — person's name, pet's name, day of week. Circle the correct reason for each sentence. The first one has been done for you.

1. Tomorrow will be <u>Wednesday</u>.
   Person   Pet   (Day)

2. My brother's name is <u>Steve</u>.
   Person   Pet   Day

3. Our horse, <u>Lightning</u>, had a pony.
   Person   Pet   Day

4. She has a pretty cat named <u>Tabby</u>.
   Person   Pet   Day

5. Do you have a game on <u>Friday</u>?
   Person   Pet   Day

6. The new boy is <u>Paul Carson</u>.
   Person   Pet   Day

7. Have you seen my dog <u>Rover</u>?
   Person   Pet   Day

8. <u>Mark</u>, <u>David</u>, and <u>Bob</u> are playing soccer.
   Person   Pet   Day

9. <u>Sarah Dawson</u> is a good speller.
   Person   Pet   Day

10. Our math test will be on <u>Tuesday</u>.
    Person   Pet   Day

11. They bought a new horse named <u>Prince</u>.
    Person   Pet   Day

12. There will be no music on <u>Thursday</u>.
    Person   Pet   Day

NAME _____ DATE_____

Read each sentence. Circle the words that need capital letters. Write the circled words with the needed capital letters on the lines at the end of the sentence. The first one has been done for you.

1. Summer begins in (june) _June_____

2. I was born in november. _____

3. Christmas is in december. _____

4. We like to swim in july and august. _____

5. It is cold in january. _____

6. february is a short month. _____

7. We start school in august or september. _____

8. We have turkey near the end of november. _____

9. It is fun to dress up in october. _____

10. "april showers bring may flowers." _____

11. He was born in march. _____

12. There is no school in july and august. _____

_____

13. My parents were married in december. _____

14. George Washington was born in february. _____

15. My friend is coming to visit in september. _____

NAME_____ DATE_____

Read each sentence. Circle the words that need capital letters. Put the capital letter needed above the circled word. The first one has been done for you.

1. There is no school on thanksgiving and christmas.

2. We have fun on valentine's day.

3. Do you open your gifts on christmas eve or christmas day?

4. may day is the first day of may.

5. We do not have school on memorial day.

6. easter is a special Sunday.

7. We should be nice to our parents on mother's day and father's day.

8. new year's day is the first day of a new year.

9. Boys and girls have fun on halloween.

10. There are parties on new year's eve.

11. labor day comes in September.

12. palm sunday comes before easter sunday.

13. Most people wear green on st. patrick's day.

14. We honor Washington and Lincoln on president's day.

15. hanukkah is a special time for Jewish people.

16. We play tricks on april fools' day.

17. The fourth of july is a fun holiday.

18. veteran's day and flag day are two special days.

19. Our family opens their gifts on christmas eve.

20. What are you going to dress up as on halloween?

NAME_____ DATE_____

Read each sentence. There are capital letters missing. Cross out the small letters and write the capital letter above where needed. The first one has been done for you.

1. We are going to the mountains in *N*ovember.

2. The men will begin to paint our house on wednesday.

3. They are going to visit their grandparents for thanksgiving.

4. Are you going to the beach on monday or tuesday?

5. My favorite holiday is easter.

6. We honor our mothers on mother's day and our fathers on father's day.

7. He was born in the month of october and his sister was born in the month of august.

8. We celebrate valentine's day and president's day in february.

9. What are you going to do on friday?

10. There is no school on memorial day and labor day.

11. st. patrick's day comes in march.

12. We are going to a picnic on the fourth of july.

13. Were you born in june or july?

14. There is no practice on saturday.

15. When is easter this year?

NAME_____ DATE_____

Read each group of words. Find the word in each group that should be capitalized. Cross out the small letter and write the correct capital letter above it. The first one has been done for you.

1.	sandwich	**N**~~n~~ovember	roof
2.	christmas	rug	television
3.	cake	desk	july
4.	thursday	house	picture
5.	window	plant	labor day
6.	glass	easter	colors
7.	paints	pencil	sunday
8.	chair	table	january
9.	logs	thanksgiving	pens
10.	september	sofa	lamp
11.	mother	ruler	father's day
12.	dress	friday	paper
13.	farm	dishes	april
14.	tuesday	game	bird
15.	dog	hair	valentine's day

NAME_____ DATE_____

Put in the beginning letter that is needed for each day, month, or holiday. Cross out each letter in the Letter Box. The letters will only be used once. The first one has been done for you.

LETTER BOX

A	D	F	J	M̶	O	S	T	V
A	E	H	J	M	P	S	T	W
C	F	J	M	N	S	T	V	

1. **M**arch
2. __hursday
3. __hristmas
4. __ecember
5. __onday
6. __ovember
7. __unday
8. __alloween
9. __uesday
10. __pril
11. __alentine's Day
12. __ctober
13. __aturday

14. __uly
15. __hanksgiving
16. __eptember
17. __riday
18. __alm Sunday
19. __ebruary
20. __other's Day
21. __aster
22. __une
23. __ednesday
24. __ugust
25. __anuary
26. __eteran's Day

NAME_____ DATE_____

Read each sentence in Part A. There are extra capital letters in each sentence. Rewrite the sentences in Part B with the needed capital letters. The first one has been done for you.

PART A

1. My New Cat Is Named Midnight.
2. They Got Married In June.
3. The Women Are Going Shopping On Friday.
4. Bob, John, Matt, And Sam Are Playing Soccer.
5. Some Of The Holidays Are Valentine's Day, Memorial Day, Christmas Eve, Labor Day, And Palm Sunday.
6. I Like To Ride My Horse Fury.
7. Mary And Jane Are Doing Their Homework.
8. Mother's Birthday Is In December.
9. Children Dress In Costumes On Halloween.
10. The Artist Will Show His Work On Friday, Saturday And Sunday.

PART B

1. *My new cat is named Midnight.*
2. _____
3. _____
4. _____
5. _____
6. _____
7. _____
8. _____
9. _____
10. _____

NAME_____ DATE_____

TEST

Read each sentence. On the line following the sentence write the reason why the underlined word is capitalized. The first one has been done for you.

Person's Name   Month
Pet's Name   Holiday
Day

1. We saw <u>Dan</u> at the store. *Person's Name*_____

2. I was born in <u>November</u>. _____

3. Tomorrow it will be <u>Wednesday</u>. _____

4. My dog, <u>Rover</u>, is chasing a car. _____

5. We have fun on <u>Christmas</u>. _____

6. There is no school on <u>Labor Day</u>. _____

7. <u>Bob</u>, <u>Jane</u>, and <u>Karen</u> are absent today. _____

8. That horse, <u>Lightning</u>, is very fast. _____

9. On <u>Friday</u> we are going to visit our friends. _____

10. Do we start school in <u>August</u> or <u>September</u>? _____

11. Where did you put <u>Bill's</u> baseball? _____

12. Are you coming for dinner on <u>Sunday</u>? _____

13. <u>Fourth of July</u> is a special day. _____

14. Our cat, <u>Boots</u>, is fun to play with. _____

15. There is no school in <u>July</u>. _____

NAME_____ DATE_____

Read each sentence. There are capital letters missing. Cross out the small letter and put the correct capital letter above it. The first one has been done for you.

1. Our principal is *M*r. Yates.

2. mr. and mrs. Cooper live on our street.

3. My friend's name is Barbara g. Dixon.

4. We visited with dr. and mrs. Anderson.

5. His boss is mr. t. Olson.

6. mr. Smith, dr. Brown, and mr. Warren are playing golf.

7. miss Randall and ms. Simpson went to the museum.

8. dr. Walker is a good dentist.

9. mrs. j. Browning and mrs. l. Thompson are nurses at the hospital.

10. His initials are d.s.t.

11. ms. Carson is our teacher this year.

12. Our family doctor is dr. Thomas.

NAME_____ DATE_____

Read each sentence. Fill in the blanks with an abbreviation title from below. Use each abbreviation title at least once. Make sure your sentences make sense!

Mr.   Ms.
Mrs.   Rev.
Miss   Dr.

1. Our new pastor is _____ Carlson.

2. _____ and _____ Brown are on vacation.

3. _____ Jones is my music teacher.

4. _____ Marks is a very nice doctor.

5. _____ Samuels and _____ Cooper have gone to play golf.

6. We have a new dentist named _____ Rose.

7. The minister at that church is _____ Nelson.

8. _____ Reed, _____ Bloom, and _____ Olson have gone shopping.

9. _____ Dawson put my broken leg in a cast.

10. _____ and _____ Long are going out to dinner.

11. _____ Weed is our new dentist.

12. _____ Ford baked cupcakes for our class.

NAME _____ DATE_____

TEST

Read each sentence. The underlined word in each sentence is capitalized because of one of the rules listed below. Please put the letter of the correct rule on the line following each sentence. The first sentence has been done for you.

a. First word of sentence
b. Pronoun "I"
c. Proper names
d. Pets names
e. Days

f. Months
g. Holidays
h. Abbreviations
i. Initials

1. Tomorrow will be <u>Wednesday</u>. _e_

2. <u>The</u> men are working on the road. _____

3. Have you seen <u>Mrs</u>. Jones lately? _____

4. Our new puppy is called <u>Lassie.</u> _____

5. May <u>I</u> go to the party? _____

6. My mother's birthday is in <u>July</u>. _____

7. They named their baby <u>Jody</u>. _____

8. Mr. <u>J. L.</u> Smith is my father's boss. _____

9. We celebrate <u>Easter</u> in the spring. _____

10. What are you going to do on <u>Sunday</u>? _____

11. He went to see <u>Dr</u>. Cook. _____

12. We are going to visit our grandmother in <u>April.</u> _____

13. <u>What</u> time is the meeting? _____

14. Please give this book to <u>Bob.</u> _____

15. That horse named <u>Charger</u> is quick. _____

NAME_____ DATE_____

PART A: Read each sentence. Put in the missing punctuation mark.

1. Columbus discovered America on October 12 1492.

2. Father and Mother got married on May 22 1950.

3. We visited Washington, D.C., on July 20 1980.

4. The Japanese attacked Pearl Harbor on December 7 1942.

5. My sister's birthdate is March 9 1950.

6. Mr. and Mrs. Walker adopted a new baby on January 7 1975.

7. Our neighbors went to see the musical on April 15 1978.

8. Mrs. Simpson had a baby boy on November 10 1979.

PART B: Write a sentence for each date.

1. June 16, 1981

    _____

2. October 24, 1970

    _____

3. January 11, 1979

    _____

4. December 15, 1977

    _____

5. August 12, 1980

    _____

NAME_____ DATE_____

PART A: Look at each numbered word. Find the lettered abbreviation for each numbered word. Draw a line between the word and its abbreviation.

1. Mister   a. Miss
2. Reverend   b. Dr.
3. Miss   c. Mr.
4. Doctor   d. Pres.
5. President   e. Rev.

PART B: Write a sentence for each of the abbreviations listed below.

1. Mrs.

_____

2. Miss

_____

3. Rev.

_____

4. Dr.

_____

5. Mr.

_____

6. Ms.

_____

7. Pres.

_____

NAME_____ DATE_____

Read each name. Rewrite the name on line a (for each item) as the first name, middle initial, and last name. On line b rewrite the name as first initial, middle name, and last name. On line c rewrite the name as first initial, middle initial, and last name. Lastly on line d rewrite the name as first initial, middle initial, and last initial. The first name has been done for you.

1. John William Brown

    a. John W. Brown

    b. J. William Brown

    c. J. W. Brown

    d. J. W. B.

2. Susan Marie Johnson

    a. _____

    b. _____

    c. _____

    d. _____

3. George Randall Yates

    a. _____

    b. _____

    c. _____

    d. _____

4. Robert Greg Cooper

    a. _____

    b. _____

    c. _____

    d. _____

5. Charles Richard Cook

    a. _____

    b. _____

    c. _____

    d. _____

6. Samuel Fred Moore

    a. _____

    b. _____

    c. _____

    d. _____

7. Ronald Alan Parker

    a. _____

    b. _____

    c. _____

    d. _____

8. Linda Marie Carter

    a. _____

    b. _____

    c. _____

    d. _____

NAME_____ DATE_____

TEST

Read each sentence. Put in the missing punctuation marks.

1. J F Kennedy was one of our presidents.

2. My friend's name is Ann J Brown.

3. Mr and Mrs Woods are nice neighbors.

4. The pastor of our church is Rev G Clay.

5. The head of the company is Pres Fred S Moore.

6. Is Miss Goodson coming home today?

7. Dr Jones has moved his office to Bell Street.

8. Who is B G Bloom?

9. Ms Robbins and Mrs Booth work at the hospital.

10. Our dentist's name is Dr Alan M Drake.

11. My father's name is Mr George L Mattson.

12. My mother's name is Mrs Lynn S Mattson.

CAPITALIZATION/PUNCTUATION

NAME_____ DATE_____

Read each group of words. Find the word in each group that should be capitalized. Cross out the small letter and write the correct capital letter above it.

Example: book   *T*om   girl

1. book   candy   friday

2. apple   april   frog

3. jane   cup   moon

4. fred   sun   door

5. car   store   easter

6. friend   sunday   table

7. coat   chair   october

8. christmas   stone   plate

9. lamp   toy   susan

10. paper   thursday   tub

11. dancer   chalk   smith

12. grandparents   house   december

13. jones   plant   truck

14. rug   monday   river

15. lake   star   fido

51

NAME_____ DATE_____

Read each sentence. There are capital letters missing. Circle the words missing capital letters. Rewrite the sentence in correct form on the line below the printed sentence.

1. Where did john put his new watch?

_____

2. I have to go to the doctor on friday.

_____

3. Our dog, spot, is big.

_____

4. Are you going to the store on monday or tuesday?

_____

5. susan and jane are playing a game.

_____

6. We have fun on halloween.

_____

7. Her birthday is on christmas day.

_____

8. We are going on vacation in august.

_____

9. mary, bill, fred, and jean are absent today.

_____

10. Is your birthday in october or november?

_____

11. Does bob have to stay after school?

_____

12. Father is going to take us to the movies on saturday.

_____

NAME_____ DATE_____

Rewrite each sentence correctly with the needed capital letters and punctuation marks.

1. mr and mrs Scott are going on vacation.

   _____

2. ms Thomas bought a new car.

   _____

3. dr Jones, mrs Smith, mr Wilson, ms Robertson, and miss Carter are at the meeting.

   _____

   _____

4. We saw mr and mrs Woods at the zoo.

   _____

5. Have you seen miss Cooper's blue sweater?

   _____

6. Are you going to the party at dr and mrs Booth's house?

   _____

7. Our teacher's name is ms Thomson.

   _____

8. My father's boss is pres John Warren.

   _____

NAME_____ DATE_____

PART A: Read each sentence. Please circle any words that need capital letters. Write the capital letter above each circled word. Put in any missing punctuation marks.

1. mother has gone to the store

2. when are you coming over to my house

3. mr and mrs Jones have a new baby

4. i am going to see dr Wilson today

5. we saw ms Johnson at the shopping center

6. my sister and i are going to play tennis

7. dr Smith, mr Booth, mrs Brown and miss Cooper are going out to dinner together

8. the pastor at our church is rev Paul Rogers

9. have you met mr and mrs Young

10. do you know where ms Jefferson lives

PART B: Write a sentence for each word listed.

1. Dr.

    _____

2. Mr.

    _____

3. Mrs.

    _____

4. Miss

    _____

NAME_____ DATE_____

Read each sentence. There is a capital letter missing in each sentence. Circle the letter that should be a capital, and then, write this capital letter on the numbered space that matches the sentence number. When you are finished, you will find out one thing that is important to sentences. The first one has been done for you.

__ __ **P** __ __ __ __   __ __ __ __ __ __ __
14 12 1 8 6 3 9   2 7 13 5 11 4 10

1. I saw (p)aul at the zoo yesterday.

2. labor Day comes in September.

3. It is hot in august.

4. My dog is called rover.

5. We are going to the library on tuesday.

6. The store closes early on thursday.

7. It will soon be easter.

8. She said that i may leave now.

9. My horse, lightning, is a fast runner.

10. Sometimes school begins in september.

11. His name is eric.

12. It often rains in april.

13. Where is tom today?

14. I like christmas.

NAME_____ DATE_____

TEST

Read each sentence. Put in the missing punctuation marks. Cross out the small letters and write the correct capital letter above where needed.

1. Mother and Father were married on september 26 1948.

2. sarah, susan, and glenda have gone to see a movie.

3. mr ferris, mr little, and dr cook have gone to a meeting.

4. memorial day and labor day are two holidays.

5. I named my new horse patches.

6. Are you going to visit your grandmother on tuesday or friday?

7. joyce and kevin are two new students in our class.

8. dr and mrs clark are going on vacation in june and in august.

9. mrs. brown had twins on march 31 1978.

10. Our principal's name is mr g moore.

11. Is ms martin a good teacher?

12. The new head of the company is pres d owens.

13. Our new neighbors are rev and mrs long.

14. paul, keith, jim, and steve are playing basketball.

15. valentine's day and president's day come in february.

OVERVIEW

A. **CAPITALIZATION**—Additional proper nouns (streets, cities, states, titles, schools)

   1. **Introduction**—Put sentences on the chalkboard. The capital letters for each *street* should be in a different color chalk. Students should copy the sentences once discussion is finished.

      Sentences:

      a. Jean lives on Lime Street.

      b. Do you live on Carson Road or Carson Avenue?

      c. Our friends live on Florida Avenue.

      d. Father works on Simpson Boulevard

      e. Their new house is on Hanson Court.

      f. That store is on Sixth Place.

      g. My grandparents live on Park Lane.

      h. There are ten houses on Fisher Drive.

   2. Worksheet #39

   3. Worksheet #40

   4. **Boardwork/Introduction**—Put sentences on the chalkboard with *cities* and *states*. Put the capital letters in with a different color chalk. Students should copy the sentences after discussion is completed.

      Sentences:

      a. We live in _____, _____.

      b. I once lived in Missouri.

      c. Her grandparents live in Denver, Colorado.

      d. They are on vacation in Miami, Florida.

      e. Have you ever been to Washington, D.C.?

      f. Oranges are grown in California and Florida.

      g. It is usually hot in Las Vegas, Nevada.

      h. He is flying to Chicago.

   5. Worksheet #41

6. Worksheet #42

7. **Boardwork/Introduction** — Put sentences on the chalkboard with *schools* and *titles*. The capitals should be in a different color chalk. Students are to copy the sentences onto their paper after discussion is completed.

   Sentences:

   a. My sister goes to South High School.

   b. We go to Park School.

   c. He is going to attend Brown University.

   d. My cousin is going to Washington College.

   e. Our soccer team is playing Jefferson School today.

   f. Her brother is at Lincoln Junior High School.

   g. His boss is President Cooper.

   h. Father and Mother are on a trip.

8. **Boardwork** — Write the names of several schools in your area on the chalkboard with all small letters (include junior high and high schools). Students are to copy these onto their papers, putting in the needed capital letters.

9. Worksheet #43

10. **Activity** — Give the students an old workbook, magazine or newspaper page and different colors of pens, pencils or markers. A different color is assigned to each capitalization rule: streets, cities, states. Students are to circle all examples of each capitalization rule with the correct color.

11. **Boardwork** — Read each sentence. Copy the sentences putting in the needed capital letters.

    Sentences:

    a. Dr. Rogers moved his office from east avenue in san francisco to western boulevard in phoenix.

    b. I attended sunshine nursery school.

    c. Have you ever visited new york?

    d. She went to blair college.

    e. They live on nelson street.

    f. My friend lives in georgia.

    g. President Lincoln lived in Illinois.

    h. The state of texas is in the south.

12. Worksheet #44

13. Worksheet #45

14. **Activity** — "Grab Bag" — Put at least 20 cards that have words with all lower case letters in the bag (include cities, states, streets, schools). Students take turns drawing the cards. The player tells whether the word should or should not be capitalized. If correct, he keeps the card; if incorrect, the card is returned to the bag. The game is concluded once all the cards have been drawn. The winner is the player with the most cards.

15. Worksheet #46

16. Worksheet #47 — TEST

B. **PUNCTUATION** — Periods in all abbreviations (St., Ave., Wed., Dec.)

1. **Introduction** — Explain to the students that days, months and thoroughfares can be abbreviated. Write the current day of the week on the chalkboard and then the abbreviation for it with the period in a different color chalk. Next, write the current month of the year on the chalkboard and then write the abbreviation for it with the period in a different color chalk. If the current month does not have an abbreviation, put a month on the chalkboard that does. Finally, list all the *thoroughfares* on the chalkboard with the periods in a different color chalk. Students are to copy these onto paper.

   a. Avenue   Ave.

   b. Boulevard Blvd.

   c. Drive   Dr.

   d. Place   Pl.

   e. Court   Ct.

   f. Road   Rd.

   g. Street   St.

   h. Lane   Ln.

2. Worksheet #48

3. Worksheet #49

4. **Boardwork** — Write the days of the week on the chalkboard with their abbreviations next to them. Have the students take turns coming up to the chalkboard and putting the periods in, using a different color chalk. Then students should copy the days and their abbreviations onto paper.

   a. Monday   Mon.

   b. Tuesday   Tues.

   c. Wednesday Wed.

   d. Thursday Thurs.

e. Friday   Fri.

f. Saturday   Sat.

g. Sunday   Sun.

5. Worksheet #50

6. Worksheet #51

7. **Boardwork** — Copy the sentences from the chalkboard. Put the abbreviation for each day of the week in the sentences rather than the whole word.

   Sentences:

   a. I went to the dentist on Monday morning.

   b. On Saturday my parents went to see a play in Chicago.

   c. Last Thursday I played tennis with my friend.

   d. Are you going to see a movie on Friday night?

   e. We went to visit my grandmother on Sunday afternoon.

   f. I am going to a birthday party Saturday morning.

   g. They are leaving on Wednesday to go to Hawaii.

   h. Next Tuesday our class is having a test.

8. Worksheet #52

9. Worksheet #53

10. **Boardwork** — Write the months of the year on the chalkboard with their abbreviations next to them. Have students take turns coming up to the chalkboard and putting in the periods using a different color chalk. Then, students are to copy the months and their abbreviations onto paper.

    a. January   Jan.

    b. February   Feb.

    c. March   Mar.

    d. April   Apr.

    e. May   ---

    f. June   ---

    g. July   ---

    h. August   Aug.

    i. September Sept.

    j. October   Oct.

    k. November Nov.

    l. December Dec.

11. Worksheet #54

12. Worksheet #55

13. **Activity** — "Months Relay" — The teacher should make up 30 cards. On each card should be written a month, an abbreviation with a period, or an abbreviation without a period (no abbreviation cards for May, June, and July). The students are given the cards with the months on them. The abbreviation cards (with and without the periods) are placed along the chalkboard ledge in random order. The students are divided into two teams of six students per team. On the command of "go", the first student from each side races to the chalkboard ledge and selects the correct abbreviation for their month. Then, they return to the back of their lines and the next students proceed. The first team to finish is the winner, providing each member has chosen the correct card. It should be explained to the students that if their month has no abbreviation, they should race to the chalkboard ledge, touch it, and return to the back of the line.

14. Worksheet #56

15. Worksheet #57 — TEST

C. **PUNCTUATION-Comma between City and State**

1. **Introduction** — Write the name of the local city and state on the chalkboard. Put the comma in using a different color chalk while explaining to the students why a comma separates the two words. List other cities from the local state on the chalkboard. Have students come to the chalkboard and put in the commas. Then, have the students copy all cities and states onto their papers.

   Examples: Los Angeles, California
   San Diego, California
   Pasadena, California

2. **Boardwork** — The students are to copy the sentences from the chalkboard. They are to put in the missing punctuation marks.

   Sentences:

   a. The Johnson family is moving to Albany New York.

   b. My uncle lives in Dallas Texas.

   c. Marquette University is located in Milwaukee Wisconsin.

   d. They went to Honolulu Hawaii on vacation.

   e. Have you ever visited Las Vegas Nevada?

   f. She was born in Salt Lake City Utah.

   g. My grandparents live in Tampa Florida.

   h. When are you moving to Detroit Michigan?

3. Worksheet #58

4. **Boardwork**—Write several cities and states on the chalkboard. Omit the commas. The students are to copy the cities and states and put in the missing punctuation mark.

   a. Cleveland Ohio

   b. New Orleans Louisiana

   c. Wichita Kansas

   d. Seattle Washington

   e. Lincoln Nebraska

   f. Ft. Worth Texas

   g. Flagstaff Arizona

   h. Pittsburgh Pennsylvania

   i. Boston Massachusetts

   j. Atlanta Georgia

D. PUNCTUATION—Apostrophe in Contractions

1. **Introduction**—Write the contraction *"I'm"* on the chalkboard with the apostrophe in colored chalk. Explain that the contraction is a short way of saying two words. This is done by omitting some of the letters and putting an apostrophe in place of these letters. Write the word "contraction" on the chalkboard and write the two words "I am" below the contraction in colored chalk. Next, write more contractions on the chalkboard and have students take turns giving the two words that each contraction is made from. Cross out the omitted letters with colored chalk and put the apostrophe above them in colored chalk. Students are to copy all of this onto their papers.

Examples:	isn't	is not
	can't	cannot
	he's	he is
	we're	we are

2. Worksheet #59

3. Worksheet #60

4. **Activity**—Puzzles—The teacher makes up rectangular cards with a jagged line on each. These lines should vary from card to card with no two lines the same. Then, the teacher writes a contraction on one side and the two words from that contraction on the other side of the card. The cards are cut on the jagged line. Next, the puzzle pieces are mixed up; and the students take turns matching the contractions with the two words that comprise them. The students read each contraction and the two words for it when a match is made.

5. **Boardwork** — Copy the sentences. Put in the missing apostrophe for each contraction. The contractions are underlined.

Sentences:

a. *Its* going to rain today.

b. We *cant* go to the party.

c. They *dont* have any fruit left at the store.

d. *Whos* at the door?

e. *Havent* you finished your work?

f. *Well* see you at the ball game.

g. *Ive* found my jacket.

h. The men *arent* working on the house today.

i. *Hed* like to get a new bike.

j. They *arent* at home.

6. **Activity** — "Double-Dip Contractions" — The teacher should make up cards resembling a double-dip ice cream cone, plus cards resembling dips of vanilla and strawberry ice cream. Two slits to hold the "ice cream" should be made in the cone about one-half inch down. Across the cone is written a contraction. The two words that make up the contraction are written on the ice cream, one word on the vanilla and one word on strawberry.

Directions: Each student gets a cone. Each student, in turn, goes to the table or pocket card holder and finds the two words that make up his contraction. He places them in the proper order in the cone. He holds up his cone and reads his contraction to the class. Also, he tells the two words that make up his contraction and what letters have been omitted for the apostrophe.

7. Worksheet #61

8. Worksheet #62 — TEST

E. **PUNCTUATION** — Apostrophe in Possessives (simple)

1. **Introduction** — Write on the chalkboard the following sentences: "The doll belongs to Susan." Below this write the words — "Susan's doll" — with the apostrophe in a different color chalk. Then, write on the chalkboard several groups of words that indicate possession, omitting the *apostrophe and s*. As you put the *apostrophe and s* in with a different color chalk, explain that we do this so that it is shorter to write. Have the students copy these onto their papers.

Examples: John's ball
Roger's bike
Linda's book
Mike's car
Mary's coat

2. Worksheet #63

3. **Boardwork** — Read each sentence. Put in the missing apostrophe mark for each underlined word.

   Sentences:
   a. *Johns* dog is barking loudly.
   b. *Mothers* jacket is missing.
   c. The *girls* shirt is torn.
   d. The *teachers* books are on the shelf.
   e. *Barbs* bike is new.
   f. *Pauls* football is caught up on the roof.
   g. The *dogs* house is falling apart.
   h. *Fathers* job is interesting.

4. **Activity** — "Puzzles" — The teacher should make up cards with a jagged line on each card. These lines should vary from card to card with no two lines the same. The teacher writes a word on one side and on the other side of the card she writes its possessive form. The cards are cut along the lines. Next, the puzzle pieces are mixed up and the students take turns matching the puzzle pieces. The students read each possessive and the word that it is made from after each match has been made.

5. Worksheet #64

6. Worksheet #65

7. Worksheet #66 — TEST

F. **REVIEW**

   1. **Boardwork** — Copy each sentence. Put in the missing capital letters and punctuation marks.

      Sentences:
      a. dr. jones is at the hospital
      b. We are moving to cleveland ohio
      c. I dont know what to do
      d. Johns bike is missing
      e. The new library is on chester ave in buffalo new york
      f. Are you going to the store on wed or thur?
      g. Were you born in sept or oct?
      h. They cant find the books

2. Worksheet #67

3. **Activity** — Do puzzle and game activities listed in the previous sections of this level.

4. Worksheet #68

5. Worksheet #69

6. Worksheet #70

7. Worksheet #71

8. Worksheet #72 — TEST #1

9. Worksheet #73 — TEST #2

NAME _____ DATE _____

Read each group of words. Write the words on the lines putting in the needed capital letters. The first one has been done for you.

1. west avenue *West Avenue* _____

2. third street _____

3. paris drive _____

4. cooper road _____

5. seventh avenue _____

6. main street _____

7. lemon court _____

8. lewis boulevard _____

9. jefferson road _____

10. avon lane _____

11. market street _____

12. texas drive _____

13. iowa street _____

14. tower place _____

15. bell drive _____

16. lake boulevard _____

17. tenth court _____

18. orange lane _____

19. kansas avenue _____

20. parker road _____

NAME_____ DATE_____

PART A: Read each sentence. Fill in the blanks.

1. I live on _____

2. My best friend lives on _____

3. Our school is on_____

4. The city library is on_____

5. The nearest fire station is on_____

PART B: Write a sentence. Circle the words that need capital letters. Write the correct capital letter above each circled word.

1. I went to the library on south street.

2. Are you going to the park on eagle avenue or boston road?

3. We live on yale court, not yale boulevard.

4. Our neighbors moved to lincoln place.

5. The new grocery store is on tenth avenue.

6. Father works on denver street.

7. Mother works on redding road.

8. My best friend lives on smith drive.

9. Have you visited the candy store on harvard court?

10. Where is oak lane?

NAME_____ DATE_____

Read each sentence. Circle the words that need capital letters. Rewrite each sentence putting in the needed capital letters. The first one has been done for you.

1. They are moving to (atlanta) (georgia)

They are moving to Atlanta, Georgia.

2. There are many fun places to visit in los angeles.

_____

3. Disneyworld is in orlando, florida.

_____

4. We are going to vacation in dallas, texas.

_____

5. He is traveling in alaska.

_____

6. Bob's parents are in honolulu, hawaii.

_____

7. Have you ever been to idaho or montana?

_____

8. My friends live in new york.

_____

9. Our neighbors moved to columbus, ohio.

_____

10. They bought that clock in san francisco, california.

_____

NAME_____ DATE_____

Read each city and state. Rewrite the word on the line with the correct capital letter. Then, try to match the cities and states. Draw a line between those you know. The first one has been done for you.

CITIES

STATES

1. denver _*Denver*_____   massachusetts _____

2. dallas _____   arizona _____

3. chicago _____   colorado _*Colorado*_____

4. phoenix _____   minnesota_____

5. milwaukee _____   washington _____

6. las vegas _____   texas _____

7. new orleans_____   tennessee _____

8. minneapolis _____   louisiana _____

9. boston _____   utah _____

10. seattle _____   illinois _____

11. salt lake city _____   michigan _____

12. detroit _____   wisconsin _____

13. st. louis _____   oklahoma_____

14. tulsa_____   missouri _____

15. memphis _____   nevada _____

NAME_____ DATE_____

Read each sentence. Circle the words that need capital letters. Write the needed capital letter above each circled word. The first one has been done for you.

1. Our class is going to see a play at west high school.

2. My friend goes to clover school.

3. Jim is playing ball at north junior high school.

4. My brother goes to central high school.

5. My sister goes to boston college.

6. My oldest brother goes to harvard university.

7. I go to miller junior high school.

8.   We are going on a field trip with students from jefferson school.

9. There is no school at smith high school today.

10. Kim goes to third avenue school.

NAME_____ DATE_____

Read each group of words. One of the word(s) should be capitalized. Cross out the small letter(s) and write the correct capital letter(s) above it. The first one has been done for you. (Read the words to students if they cannot decode them.)

1.	E̶ast S̶treet S̶chool	hotel	chair
2.	sundown	boston	carpet
3.	gas station	family	arizona
4.	drugstore	meats	simpson avenue
5.	paper	hospital	president kennedy
6.	detroit	house	plant
7.	apartment	harvard university	table
8.	company	dictionary	ohio
9.	texas	rocker	pencil
10.	magazine	knife	cooper road
11.	painting	dallas	footstool
12.	west avenue school	high school	friends
13.	cookbook	seaman	wilson boulevard
14.	los angeles	actor	soccer
15.	candy	horse	second avenue

NAME_____ DATE_____

In Column One is a list of cities and states. Rewrite each city and state on the lines in Column Two with the needed capital letters. The first one has been done for you.

COLUMN ONE   COLUMN TWO

1. detroit, michigan   _Detroit_____, _Michigan_

2. los angeles, california _____, _____

3. dallas, texas   _____, _____

4. atlanta, georgia   _____, _____

5. bangor, maine   _____, _____

6. reno, nevada   _____, _____

7. denver, colorado   _____, _____

8. dayton, ohio   _____, _____

9. phoenix, arizona   _____, _____

10. honolulu, hawaii   _____, _____

11. kansas city, missouri   _____, _____

12. buffalo, new york   _____, _____

13. lincoln, nebraska   _____, _____

14. baltimore, maryland   _____, _____

15. tulsa, oklahoma   _____, _____

NAME_____ DATE_____

Read each sentence. Write the words which are underlined beneath the correct category listed below the sentences. Each category lists a capitalization rule that we have studied. The first one has been done for you.

1. Does <u>John</u> attend <u>Brown High School</u>?

2. We visited <u>Houston</u>, <u>Texas</u>, last summer.

3. My friend, <u>Kathy</u>, moved to <u>Cooper Road</u>.

4. Have you ever been to <u>Portland</u>, <u>Washington</u>?

5. I have lived in the states of <u>Maine</u>, <u>Missouri</u>, and <u>California</u>.

6. My sister attends <u>Pepperdine University</u>.

7. Our friends live on <u>Sunset Boulevard</u>.

8. <u>Susan</u> and <u>Lisa</u> went to see the play at <u>Carson College</u>.

9. Our new office is on <u>Center Street</u> in <u>Springfield</u>, <u>Illinois</u>.

10. He teaches at <u>Washington School</u>.

NAME	STATE	SCHOOL
John		*Brown High School*

CITY	STREET

74

NAME_____ DATE_____

TEST

Read each sentence. On the lines following the sentences, tell why the underlined words are capitalized. The first one has been done for you.

1. I live on <u>Lincoln Road</u>. *Street* _____

2. They attended <u>Harvard University</u>. _____

3. The new family moved here from <u>Columbus</u>, <u>Ohio</u>. _____

4. My father's boss is <u>President</u> Jones. _____

5. Our children go to <u>Wilson School</u>. _____

6. We visited the state of <u>Minnesota</u> at Christmas. _____

7. Did you move to <u>Sanford Street</u> or <u>Sanford Avenue</u>? _____

8. They are visiting friends in <u>Miami</u>, <u>Florida</u>. _____

9. My dentist is <u>Dr</u>. Johnson. _____

10. The store is located on <u>Capitol Boulevard</u>. _____

11. Our new pastor is <u>Reverend</u> Lewis. _____

12. Last year I went to <u>Honolulu</u>, <u>Hawaii</u>, on vacation _____

NAME_____ DATE_____

PART A: Match the numbered word to its lettered abbreviation by drawing a line between the two.

1. Street   a. Dr.

2. Court   b. Ave.

3. Boulevard   c. Pl.

4. Place   d. Rd.

5. Avenue   e. Blvd.

6. Road   f. Ln.

7. Drive   g. Ct.

8. Lane   h. St.

PART B: Write each of the words from above on a line. Then, write its correct abbreviation across from it.

1. _____   _____

2. _____   _____

3. _____   _____

4. _____   _____

5. _____   _____

6. _____   _____

7. _____   _____

8. _____   _____

CAPITALIZATION/PUNCTUATION

WS#49

NAME_____ DATE_____

Read each sentence. Put in the missing punctuation marks.

1. Tony lives on Elm St in Denver.

2. Is your school on Pacific Ave or Pacific St?

3. They moved the store from Orange Blvd to Delta Ave last week.

4. Our friends live on Summer Ct out in the country.

5. When did you move to Tower Dr?

6. The company moved from Walnut Rd to Highland Dr last month.

7. Our neighbors once lived on Third Ave in New York City.

8. Does Sarah live on Jackson Dr?

9. Where is Parker Ln?

10. We go to a dentist on Thomas Ct in Dayton.

11. She lives on Warren Blvd in the city.

12. My grandparents live on Ivy Ln in Memphis, Tennessee.

13. Where is Lookout Dr?

14. Her school is on Beverly Blvd.

15. When did you move to Market Ln?

77

NAME_____ DATE_____

DAYS OF THE WEEK

PART A: These are the short names (abbreviations) for the days of the week. Put a period after them. Then write the day on the line after the abbreviation.

1. Mon _____

2. Tues _____

3. Wed _____

4. Thur _____

5. Fri _____

6. Sat _____

7. Sun _____

PART B: Choose four of the days and write a sentence for each day. Write the abbreviations for each day in the (   ) at the end of each line.

1. _____

_____(   )

2. _____

_____(   )

3. _____

_____(   )

4. _____

_____(   )

NAME_____ DATE_____

Read each sentence. Put in the missing punctuation marks.

1. On Sat we went to the beach.

2. We went to see a movie on Fri evening.

3. The children went to the park on Wed afternoon.

4. Are you going to the ball game on Mon or Tues ?

5. Our family went on a picnic on Sun at noon.

6. My mother and I went shopping on Thur night.

7. Did your class go to the museum on Fri ?

8. We are leaving on vacation on Sat of next week.

9. They went out to dinner on Mon night.

10. Are you going to the library on Wed or Thur afternoon?

11. Next Wed is Bill's birthday.

12. Sharon and Carol went to see the musical on Thur evening.

13. Are you going to play basketball with us on Sat ?

14. On Tues there will be no school.

NAME_____ DATE_____

PART A: Match the numbered word to its lettered abbreviation by drawing a line between the two.

1.	Thursday	a.	Sun.
2.	Monday	b.	Tues.
3.	Saturday	c.	Sat.
4.	Wednesday	d.	Thur.
5.	Sunday	e.	Fri.
6.	Friday	f.	Mon.
7.	Tuesday	g.	Wed.

PART B: Write each of the days of the week in order on the lines (begin with Sunday). Then, write its correct abbreviation next to it.

1. _____   _____

2. _____   _____

3. _____   _____

2. _____   _____

4. _____   _____

5. _____   _____

6. _____   _____

7. _____   _____

NAME_____ DATE_____

Read each sentence. Write the day of the week that fits each blank in the puzzle. Unscramble the starred (*) letters to find a day of the week. Write the abbreviation for each day of the week on the line after its place in the puzzle.

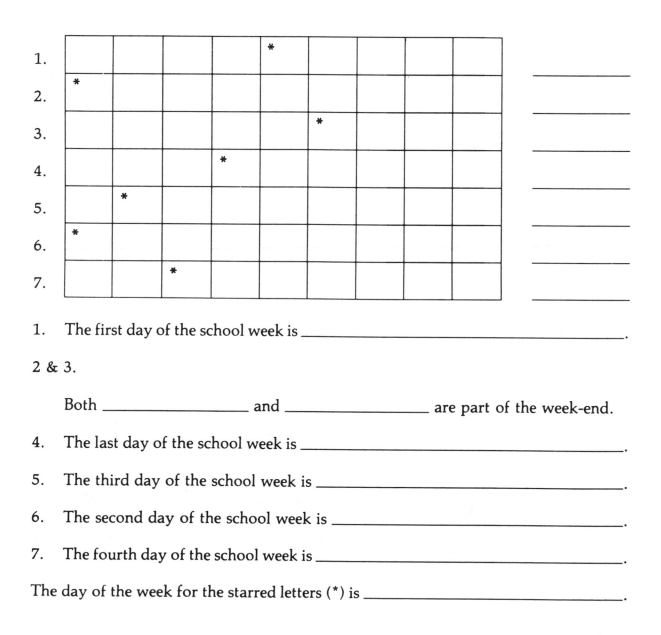

1.   The first day of the school week is _____.

2 & 3.

   Both _____ and _____ are part of the week-end.

4.   The last day of the school week is _____.

5.   The third day of the school week is _____.

6.   The second day of the school week is _____.

7.   The fourth day of the school week is _____.

The day of the week for the starred letters (*) is _____.

NAME_____ DATE_____

Read each sentence. Write the full word for each month.

1. Jan. is for _____.

2. Feb. is for _____.

3. Mar. is for _____.

4. Apr. is short for _____.

5. _____, _____ and

   _____ do not have abbreviations.

6. Aug. means _____.

7. Sept. is for _____.

8. School starts in _____.

9. Oct. is short for _____.

10. Nov. means _____.

11. Dec. is short for _____.

12. Christmas comes in _____.

13. A new year begins in _____.

14. Thanksgiving comes in _____.

15. Halloween comes in _____.

16. My birthday is in _____.

NAME_____ DATE_____

Read each sentence. Put in the missing punctuation marks.

1. In Dec we celebrate Christmas.

2. July and Aug are summer months.

3. Last Feb our friends moved to another town.

4. Marie was born on Oct 13, 1970.

5. We may go on vacation in Aug or Sept of this year.

6. My parents were married on Nov 23rd.

7. In Jan it can be very cold.

8. Our neighbors had a baby boy on Mar 18th.

9. Last Apr we visited Disneyland.

10. It was hot in Sept when we started school

11. Dec, Jan and Feb are winter months.

12. In Oct we celebrate Halloween.

13. In Nov Bill will be nine years old.

14. In Feb we celebrate Valentine's Day.

15. This coming Jan we are going skiing in Colorado.

NAME_____ DATE_____

PART A: Match the numbered word to its lettered abbreviation by drawing a line between the two.

1. March   a. Dec.
2. October   b. Jan.
3. January   c. Sept.
4. August   d. Apr.
5. December   e. Nov.
6. September   f. Mar.
7. February   g. Oct.
8. April   h. Aug.
9. November   i. Feb.

PART B: Write each of the months of the year in order on the lines (begin with January). Then, write the correct abbreviations next to them. **Remember** that three of the months do not have abbreviations.

1. _____   _____

2. _____   _____

3. _____   _____

2. _____   _____

4. _____   _____

5. _____   _____

6. _____   _____

7. _____   _____

8. _____   _____

9. _____   _____

10. _____   _____

11. _____   _____

12. _____   _____

NAME_____ DATE_____

TEST

PART A: Read each sentence. The words that are underlined are abbreviations. On the line following each sentence, please indicate whether the underlined word is an abbreviation for a *thoroughfare, day* or *month*. Use this code:
Thoroughfare — T
Day — D
Month — M

The first one has been done for you.

1. On <u>Tues</u>. we went to visit the zoo. ___*D*___

2. Last <u>Oct</u>. we went on a hayride. _____.

3. Is your new house on River <u>Rd</u>.? _____

4. In <u>Jan</u>. it may snow. _____.

5. Will you go to lunch with me on <u>Wed</u>.? _____

6. Dr. Johnson works in an office on Carpenter <u>Blvd</u>. each day . _____

7. Were you born in <u>Aug</u>. or <u>Sept</u>.? _____

8. Our friends moved to Michigan <u>Ave</u>. in Chicago. _____

9. On <u>Sat</u>. we took a trip to the mountains. _____

10. The boys will play soccer on <u>Thur</u>. afternoon. _____

PART B: Read each word. Write its correct abbreviation on the line next to it.

1. Street   _____

2. December   _____

3. Monday   _____

4. February   _____

5. Court   _____

6. April   _____

7. Friday   _____

8. Place   _____

9. November   _____

10. Sunday   _____

NAME_____ DATE_____

Read each sentence. Put in the missing punctuation marks where they are needed. Some of the sentences are correct and can be left as they are.

1. I have lived in Kansas City Missouri and Los Angeles California.

2. They went to visit friends in Atlanta.

3. Are you going to San Francisco or San Diego California for your vacation?

4. When are you going to Tulsa?

5. I cannot go on the class trip to Washington.

6. Have you ever visited Philadelphia Pennsylvania?

7. Colorado is a pretty state.

8. The meeting will be in Chicago Illinois.

9. I would like to visit New York City New York.

10. We went to visit our uncle and aunt in Fargo North Dakota.

11. They are going to drive to Texas during Easter vacation.

12. Mr. and Mrs. Moore are moving to Hartford Connecticut.

13. Bob is going to visit his friend in Columbus Ohio.

14. Have you ever been to Mississippi?

NAME_____ DATE_____

Match the **numbered** contraction to the **lettered** two words it is made from by drawing a line between them. The first one has been done for you.

1. Who's	a. It is
2. What's	b. They would
3. They'd	c. Cannot
4. We'll	d. We have
5. Won't	e. Do not
6. Shouldn't	f. They have
7. He's	g. Will not
8. We're	h. You would
9. They've	i. Are not
10. She'd	j. What is
11. Aren't	k. I am
12. Can't	l. I have
13. Haven't	m. He is
14. It's	n. Would not
15. I'm	o. Who is
16. We've	p. She would
17. Wouldn't	q. Should not
18. I've	r. We are
19. Don't	s. Have not
20. You'd	t. We will

NAME_____ DATE_____

Write a contraction for each of the following words. Cross out the omitted letters. Example: is n⌀t — isn't. The first one has been done for you.

1. are n⌀t   *aren't*_____

2. we will   _____

3. they have   _____

4. you would   _____

5. we would   _____

6. were not   _____

7. It is   _____

8. have not   _____

9. cannot   _____

10. he is   _____

11. I have   _____

12. do not   _____

13. she is   _____

14. I am   _____

15. should not   _____

NAME_____ DATE_____

Rewrite these contractions into two words. Write the two words on the lines next to each contraction. Example: isn't — is not. The first one has been done for you.

1. I've   *I*   *have*

2. don't   _____   _____

3. it's   _____   _____

4. aren't   _____   _____

5. we'll   _____   _____

6. she's   _____   _____

7. haven't   _____   _____

8. won't   _____   _____

9. he'd   _____   _____

10. they've   _____   _____

11. we're   _____   _____

12. can't   _____   _____

13. who's   _____   _____

14. I'm   _____   _____

15. we've   _____   _____

NAME_____ DATE_____

TEST

Read each sentence. Cross out the two words that are underlined and write the contraction for these two words above them. The first one has been done for you.

1. We ~~have not~~ found the lost books. *haven't*

2. They would like to go to see that movie.

3. He is playing baseball.

4. You are a nice person.

5. Our neighbors are not coming to the picnic.

6. We will see you at the play.

7. Mother is not going shopping on Friday.

8. You would really have fun at the party.

9. What is happening at school?

10. I will not be able to stay overnight at your house.

11. She does not know how to sew.

12. You did not do your homework.

13. We have bought a new car.

14. I am getting a pony for my birthday.

15. He could not eat all of his supper.

NAME_____ DATE_____

Look at each word listed below. On the line next to each word write the word with an apostrophe and s to show possession. The first one has been done for you.

1. Jean   *Jean's*_____

2. boy   _____

3. brother   _____

4. Mark   _____

5. Jason   _____

6. teacher   _____

7. girl   _____

8. Bill   _____

9. Mother   _____

10. dog   _____

11. Sam   _____

12. Kathy   _____

13. sister   _____

14. Father   _____

15. Carol   _____

NAME_____ DATE_____

Match the **numbered** word to its **lettered** possessive by drawing a line between them.

1.	Father	a.	Beth's
2.	Pat	b.	Rick's
3.	Craig	c.	cat's
4.	boy	d.	airplane's
5.	Bob	e.	Pat's
6.	cat	f.	Dick's
7.	teacher	g.	neighbor's
8.	Beth	h.	Bob's
9.	neighbor	i.	boat's
10.	Sue	j.	Craig's
11.	airplane	k.	principal's
12.	Rick	l.	Father's
13.	principal	m.	Sue's
14.	Dick	n.	boy's
15.	boat	o.	teacher's

NAME_____ DATE_____

Read each sentence. On the line following the sentence, write the possessive for the underlined word. The first one has been done for you.

1. That house belongs to <u>Bob</u>. *Bob's* house

2. The doll belongs to <u>Mary</u>. _____ doll.

3. The dress belongs to my <u>sister</u>. my _____ dress

4. The car belongs to the <u>teacher</u>. the _____ car

5. That baseball belongs to <u>Tom</u>. _____ baseball

6. The puzzle belongs to <u>Karen</u>. _____ puzzle

7. The rattle belongs to the <u>baby</u>. the _____ rattle

8. That horse belongs to our <u>neighbor</u>. our _____ horse

9. The watch belongs to <u>Laura</u>. _____ watch

10. That typewriter belongs to Mrs. <u>Johnson</u>. Mrs. _____ typewriter

11. The flashlight belongs to the <u>boy</u>. the _____ flashlight

12. That boat belongs to Mr. <u>Cooper</u>. Mr. _____ boat

NAME_____ DATE_____

TEST

Read each sentence. Put in the missing punctuation mark.

1. Have you seen Sallys blue sweater?

2. That boys jacket fell on the ground.

3. The suns rays are hot.

4. Where is Jacks homework?

5. That trees leaves are dying.

6. Mothers chocolate cookies taste good.

7. What happened to Teds bike?

8. This is Carols new car.

9. Where is Toms reading book?

10. Marys t.v. set is broken.

11. Did you find Marks baseball?

12. Where are Fathers car keys?

13. Is this Karens math paper?

14. Tomorrow is Bills birthday party.

15. Here is Lindas purse.

NAME_____ DATE_____

Read each sentence. Write in the missing words. Remember the capital letters.

1. I live in the city of _____.

2. I live in the state of _____.

3. We write the city with the state like this: _____

   _____.

4. I live on _____.

5. Los Angeles is in the state of _____.

6. Dallas is in the state of _____.

7. Chicago is in the state of _____.

8. A state near my state is _____.

9. _____ is another city in my state.

10. _____ is a city in the state of New York.

11. _____ is a city in the state of Nevada.

12. _____ is a city in the state of Tennessee.

13. The name of our school is _____

14. It is on _____.

15. How many capital letters are on this page? _____.

NAME_____ DATE_____

ABBREVIATIONS

On the line next to each abbreviation write the word for which it stands. Cross out the word in the WORD BOX once you have used it. The first one has been done for you.

1. Mich. *Michigan*
2. Wed. _____
3. Sept. _____
4. Tex. _____
5. N.Y. _____
6. Feb. _____
7. Ave. _____
8. Ill. _____
9. Mar. _____
10. Rd. _____
11. Mon. _____
12. Nov. _____
13. Cal. _____
14. Fri. _____
15. Aug. _____
16. Tues. _____
17. N.D. _____
18. Oct. _____
19. St. _____
20. Sat. _____
21. Fla. _____
22. Dr. _____
23. Apr. _____
24. Wash. _____
25. Dec. _____
26. Sun. _____
27. Blvd. _____
28. May _____
29. Thur. _____
30. Jan. _____

November	August	Wednesday	Saturday
Drive	~~Michigan~~	October	February
Texas	December	Sunday	Boulevard
Thursday	Monday	New York	California
Friday	Florida	Street	Washington
Road	Avenue	Tuesday	March
Illinois	May	North Dakota	April
	September	January	

96

NAME_____ DATE_____

Read each sentence. Fill in the blank with an abbreviation. Remember the punctuation marks!

1. The first day of this month was _____.

2. A _____ will be the last day of the month.

3. Thanksgiving is always on a _____ _____.

4. Labor Day is always on a _____.

5. _____ is the second day of the week.

6. _____ is the first day of the week.

7. _____ is the fifth day of the week.

8. Christmas comes in _____.

9. New Year's Day is in _____.

10. School started in _____.

11. _____ is the fourth month.

12. _____ is the seventh month.

13. _____ is the first month.

14. _____ is the tenth month.

15. _____ is the fifth month.

NAME_____ DATE_____

PART A: On the line next to each contraction, write the two words that it is made from.

1 . can't   _____   6. he's   _____

2 . wasn't   _____   7. I'll   _____

3 . I'm   _____   8. we've   _____

4 . they're   _____   9. weren't   _____

5 . hadn't   _____   10. you're   _____

PART B: Read each sentence. Write the needed contraction on each line. It is made from the two words listed below the line.

1. _____ going to the circus.
    I am

2. My cousin _____ going.
          is not

3. We _____ met our new neighbors yet.
    have not

4. She _____ in school today.
    was not

5. _____ going to play football.
    He is

6. _____ see you at the park.
    We will

7. _____ bought a new house.
    They have

8. Ben _____ finish his homework.
    could not

9. _____ meet you at the restaurant.
    I will

10. Karen _____ get the job.
    did not

NAME_____ DATE_____

This worksheet is all about abbreviations. Read each sentence and fill in the blank with the correct abbreviation. Then write the numbered letter on the correct numbered space below. The first one has been done for you.

$$\underline{}\ \underline{}\ \underline{}\ \underline{}\ \underline{E}\ \underline{}\ \underline{}\ \underline{}\ \underline{}\ \underline{}\ \underline{}\ \underline{}\ \underline{}$$
$$7\ \ 2\ \ 2\ \ 10\ \ 4\ \ 8\ \ 6\ \ 3\ \ 11\ \ 6\ \ 5\ \ 9\ \ 1$$

1. The abbreviation for the third day of the week is _T_ _U_ _E_.
                                                                $\overline{4}$

2. ____ ____ ____. is the abbreviation for August.
   $\overline{3}$

3. Halloween comes in ____ ____ ____.
                       $\overline{5}$

4. ____ ____. is the abbreviation for Road.
   $\overline{10}$

5. Many people go to church on ____ ____ ____.
                               $\overline{1}$

6. Thanksgiving comes in ____ ____ ____.
                                 $\overline{8}$

7. Labor Day comes in ____ ____ ____ ____.
                                 $\overline{11}$

8. The last day of the school week is ____ ____ ____.
                                          $\overline{6}$

9. The first month of the year is ____ ____ ____.
                                       $\overline{9}$

10. ____ ____ ____ ____. is the abbreviation for Boulevard.
    $\overline{2}$

11. The abbreviation for Avenue is ____ ____ ____.
                                   $\overline{7}$

NAME_____ DATE_____

TEST #1

Read each sentence. On the line following the sentence indicate why the underlined word is capitalized. Use this code.

Thoroughfare = T   City = C   State = S

School = Sc.   Title = T

1. I have lived in <u>Connecticut</u>._____

2. He lives in <u>Pittsburgh</u>. _____

3. They go to <u>Center Street School</u>. _____

4. Bill's boss is <u>President</u> Chapman. _____

5. We live on <u>Stanton Boulevard</u>. _____

6. <u>Alabama</u> and <u>Mississippi</u> are in the South. _____

7. Kathy works on <u>Linden Road</u>. _____

8. Chuck and Don attend <u>Carver High School</u>. _____

9. My friend is visiting <u>San Diego</u>. _____

10. Our pastor is <u>Reverend</u> Carlson. _____

11. My cousin is going to <u>Brown University</u>. _____

12. <u>Minnesota</u> and <u>Wisconsin</u> are in the north. _____

13. Our grandparents moved to <u>Silverlake Avenue</u>. _____

14. The little girl goes to <u>Happytime Nursery School</u>. _____

15. We are going to <u>Las Vegas</u> next week. _____

CAPITALIZATION/PUNCTUATION   WS#73

NAME_____ DATE_____

TEST #2

Read each sentence. Put in the missing punctuation mark. On the line following each sentence write the rule for adding that punctuation mark. Use this code:

Period in Abbreviations (P.A.)
Comma between city and state (C.C.S.)
Apostrophe in Contractions (A.C.)
Apostrophe in Simple Possessives (A.P.)

1. Our neighbors are on vacation in Denver Colorado. _____

2. Donnas car is new. _____

3. The fall months are Sept , Oct and November. _____

4. Pamela was born on Feb 20, 1975. _____

5. They arent at home. _____

6. Do you live on State St? _____

7. Have you ever been to Atlanta Georgia? _____

8. Are you going shopping on Wed or Fri? _____

9. Kevins football is under the sofa. _____

10. Havent you read that book yet?_____

11. Did your car break down on Maple Ave or Maple Blvd ?_____

12. My grandparents live in Miami Florida. _____

13. Dec, Jan and Feb are three of the winter months. _____

14. Anns notebook is very neat. _____

15. Why werent you at school today? _____

OVERVIEW

*For this level it is suggested that the punctuation exercises are done first, and then the capitalization exercises.

A. **CAPITALIZATION** — First word of a quoted sentence

1. **Introduction:** Write this sentence on the chalkboard: "This is our new car," said Father. The first word of the quoted sentence should have its capital letter in a different color chalk. Explain to the students that whenever there is a quoted sentence, it begins with a capital letter. Have the students give other quoted sentences. Write these on the chalkboard. Students are to copy these onto paper.

    Examples: 1. Bob said, "It is raining."

                2. "Have you seen my blue sweater?" asked Joan.

2. Worksheet #74

3. Worksheet #75

4. Worksheet #76

5. Worksheet #77 — TEST

B. **PUNCTUATION** — Commas in Series

1. **Introduction:** Write the sentence on the chalkboard: "John took a notebook, pencil, pen, and eraser to school." Explain to the students that commas are used to separate items in a series. Put the commas in with a different color chalk. Then write this sentence on the chalkboard: "John took a note, book, pencil, pen, and eraser to school." Ask the students to tell you where to put the commas. Have the students give you sentences with several items in them. Write them on the chalkboard with the commas in colored chalk. Have the students copy these sentences onto their paper.

    Examples: 1. We played tag house marbles and doctor.

                2. I read a book watched t.v. and took a bath before I went to bed.

2. Worksheet #78

3. Worksheet #79

4. **Boardwork** — Write these sentences on the chalkboard. Tell the students to

103

write each sentence on their papers as many times as there are ways of putting in the commas. Do the first one together.

Sentences:

a. Father took a snowmobile suit ski jacket boots and hat on his trip.

b. Mother went to the store and bought butter beans corn bread chocolate cookies and meat.

c. John found a box kite bird dog cake pan and cat hidden in the picture.

5. Worksheet #80

6. Worksheet #81 — TEST

C. PUNCTUATION — Comma after Yes or No

1. **Introduction:** Write this sentence on the chalkboard: "Yes, I can go to the party." Put the comma in with colored chalk. Explain to the students that a comma is put after the word *yes* or *no* when it begins the sentence. Ask the students to give sentences beginning with *yes* or *no*. Put the commas in with colored chalk. Have the students copy them onto paper.

   Examples: 1. No, you can't play ball now.

   2. Yes, we live on Oak Street.

2. Worksheet #82

3. Worksheet #83 — TEST

D. PUNCTUATION — Quotation Marks

1. **Introduction:** The teacher writes the following two sentences on the chalkboard: "What are you doing?" asked Jane; Bobby said, "I have a new bike." Explain to the students that a quotation is the exact words that someone says and that these words are set off by quotation marks. (Put the quotation marks in with a different color chalk.) Put additional quotations on the board. After discussion, the students are to copy the sentences on their papers.

Sentences:

a. Bill asked, "What time is it?"

b. The man yelled, "That building is on fire!"

c. "No, I cannot go to the play," answered Tim.

d. "We are going to the park," said Jane.

e. "Mother has gone shopping," said Barb.

f. "Where are the cookies?" asked Tom.

g. The teacher inquired, "Who lost the ball?"

h. Sam groaned, "I lost my jacket."

2. Worksheet #84

3. Worksheet #85

4. Worksheet #86

5. Worksheet #87

6. Worksheet #88 — TEST

E. PUNCTUATION — Comma in Quotations

1. **Introduction:** Put these four sentences on the chalkboard with the comma in colored chalk.

   a. Bill said, " I am going to the library."

   b. "Don't be late," said Mother.

   c. "Where are your books?" asked Mrs. Jones. Mrs. Jones asked, "Where are your books?"

   d. "That house is on fire!" exclaimed Anna. Anna exclaimed, "That house is on fire!"

   Explain to the students that the comma is used to separate a quotation from the rest of the sentence when the quotation comes last in the sentence. When the quotation comes first in the sentence these rules apply:

   question/use question mark

   exclamation/use exclamation point

   statement/use comma.

   Now put the following sentences on the chalkboard. Do them verbally with the students and go over the above rules again. Students are to copy these sentences onto paper.

   Sentences:

   a. "It is time for recess," said the teacher.

   b. Sally said, "I am walking to school today."

   c. Grandmother inquired, "What do you want for your birthday?"

   d. "We won the race!" exclaimed Carl.

   e. "How much does that cost?" asked Linda.

   f. Mark exclaimed, "I got a new bike!"

2. Worksheet #89

3. **Activity** — Make up a chart that lists the various uses of commas. Give an example of each usage. Put the comma in a different color.

Example: *COMMAS*

a. Comma in Date
   Bill was born on February 19, 1975.

b. Comma between City and State

c. Comma after Yes or No

d. Comma in a Series of Items

e. Comma in Quotations

f. Comma after words of Direct Address

4. Worksheet #90

5. Worksheet #91 — TEST

F.   PUNCTUATION — Exclamation Point

1. **Introduction:**   First, the teacher reads a definition of what an exclamation is to the students. The teacher writes an exclamatory sentence on the chalkboard (e.g., Watch out!). The exclamation point is put on the chalkboard in colored chalk. The teacher explains when exclamation points are used in sentences. Then, she puts several exclamatory sentences on the chalkboard without the exclamation points. Students are called upon to read the sentences and put in the exclamation points (in colored chalk). Lastly, they are to copy these sentences onto their paper.

   Sentences:
   a. Watch out

   b. I got a new bike

   c. That house is on fire

   d. We won the game

   e. Mom baked chocolate chip cookies

   f. I lost my book report

2. Worksheet #92

3. Worksheet #93

4. Worksheet #94 — TEST

G.   REVIEW

1. **Boardwork — Quotations**

   Students are to copy each quotation. They are to put in the missing capital letter and the quotation marks. Sentence #1 is done as a sample.

   a. Mother said, "Come and eat."

b. Mr. Jones asked, was the car green?

c. i'm too tired, grumbled Tom.

d. have you found my coat? asked Beth

e. Jane exclaimed, i got an A on the test!

f. my father is on a trip, said Bill.

g. are you going home? inquired Carl.

h. Steve replied, yes, I am.

2. Worksheet #95

3. Worksheet #96

4. Worksheet #97

5. Worksheet #98

6. Worksheet #99 — TEST

NAME_____ DATE_____

Read each sentence. Circle the word in each sentence that needs a capital letter. Write the correct capital above the circled word. The first one has been done for you.

1. ("i)can go to the game," answered Tom.

2. "what time is it?" asked Sandra.

3. The lady screamed, "please help me."

4. Mother yelled, "don't play in the mud!"

5. "may I play at the park?" asked Mary.

6. The teacher inquired, "is this the correct answer?"

7. The boys shouted, "you're out!"

8. Bill groaned, "i did the wrong homework."

9. "did you see the accident?" questioned the policeman.

10. "it is warm today," repeated Mr. Moore.

11. Lisa murmured, "excuse me, please."

12. Father said, "we are going to the movies."

13. "get out of the way," the bully yelled.

14. The principal inquired, "who started the fight?"

15. "joe started the fight," answered Kevin.

NAME_____ DATE_____

Read each sentence. Capital letters are missing. Rewrite each sentence putting in the missing capital letters.

1. "it needs to rain," said the farmer.

   _____

2. Father asked, "where are my tools?"

   _____

3. "watch out for that car!" yelled the lady.

   _____

4. The teacher said, "please be quiet."

   _____

5. Bob groaned, "i can't find my new baseball glove."

   _____

6. The coach shouted, "who is up next?"

   _____

7. "i am up next," answered David.

   _____

8. "can I please stay up later?" pleaded Karen.

   _____

NAME_____ DATE_____

Complete each quoted sentence.

1. Tom yelled, "_____."

2. "_____," said Mrs. Carson.

3. "_____?" asked Bob.

4. Sandy groaned, "_____."

5. Jean questioned, "_____?"

6. Father yelled," _____."

7. "_____," answered the boy.

8. The girls asked, "_____?"

9. Mother said, "_____."

10. "_____?" asked the teacher.

NAME_____ DATE_____

TEST

Read each sentence. Circle the words that should be capitalized. Write the correct capital letter above the circled word. The first one has been done for you.

1. *D* (did) the bell ring?" asked John.

2. "it's too late to play ball," said Tim.

3. Joe shouted, "look out!"

4. Mother called, "the cookies are done."

5. "may I go out now?" inquired Beth.

6. "hurry up!" exclaimed Father.

7. The teacher questioned, "where is your homework?"

8. "clean your room," said Mother.

9. "the weather is too hot today," groaned Lisa.

10. "are you riding your bike to school?" asked Ben.

11. Jane exclaimed, "what an exciting game!"

12. Mike asked, "may I clean the chalkboard erasers?"

13. "we lost the game by one point," grumbled Sam.

14. "that's too bad," said Dad.

15. Pat said, "i would like eggs for breakfast."

NAME_____ DATE_____

Read each sentence. Put in the missing commas.

1. Father fixed the roof the broken window the broken stair and the lamp.

2. We visited Las Vegas Los Angeles San Diego and Palm Springs on our vacation.

3. I have lived in the states of Missouri Maine Mississippi Connecticut Wisconsin California and Colorado.

4. Susan found a book key penny and pencil on her way home.

5. The horse ran up the hill ran down the hill jumped over the fence and ran through the tall grass.

6. Bill got a kite shirt baseball and game for his birthday.

7. Mother would like perfume a dress gloves shoes and purse for Christmas.

8. I ate a sandwich potato chips cookies and milk for lunch.

9. The children had a snack ran a race played baseball and did their homework after school.

10. The dog chased a car cat mailman and the children on bikes.

11. We went to visit Uncle Paul Aunt Karen Susan and Tom.

12. Father and Mother bought bread milk fruit rice potatoes meat fish and cereal at the store.

NAME_____ DATE_____

Write a sentence for each series of items. Put in the commas.

1. New York Chicago Dallas   Los Angeles   and San Francisco

_____

_____

2. books pencils paper pens and folders.

_____

_____

3. dogs cats birds turtles and fish

_____

_____

4. oranges apples pears peaches and grapes

_____

_____

5. knife fork spoon plate and glass

_____

_____

6. kite ball blocks bat and marbles

_____

_____

7. sofa chair lamp rocker and desk

_____

_____

8. California Nevada Texas Georgia and Pennsylvania

_____

_____

NAME _____ DATE_____

Read each group of words. Put in the missing commas. The first one has been done for you.

1. car, boat, plane, train, and bus

2. apple pear orange peach and banana

3. red blue green yellow purple brown black and white

4. up down in out over under and above

5. pencil book paper notebook and pen

6. seeds tree and grass

7. chair desk sofa bed and table

8. one six nine two three and five

10. sky air clouds rain snow sun and birds

11. add subtract multiply and divide

12. walk run trot gallop skip and jog

13. play ride sing run and watch

14. watch and clock

15. puzzles games blocks and books

16. meat bread eggs cake and cheese

17. milk coffee water juice and pop

18. May August September July and April

19. Monday Friday Thursday and Saturday

20. long short wide thin big little and small

NAME_____ DATE_____

TEST

Listen as your teacher reads each sentence. Put in a comma each time your teacher pauses. The first one has been done for you.

1. Mary had soup, apple pie, ice cream, and milk for lunch.

2. Mary had soup apple pie ice cream and milk for lunch.

3. Mary had soup apple pie ice cream and milk for lunch.

4. Mary had soup apple pie ice cream and milk for lunch.

5. Jack is looking for his bat baseball glove basketball hoop and cap.

6. Jack is looking for his bat baseball glove basketball hoop and cap.

7. Jack is looking for his bat baseball glove basketball hoop and cap.

8. Jack is looking for his bat baseball glove basketball hoop and cap.

9. I had toast orange juice cereal and eggs for breakfast.

10. I had toast orange juice cereal and eggs for breakfast.

NAME_____ DATE_____

Read each sentence. Put in the missing commas. The first one has been done for you.

1. No, the Johnsons are not at home.

2. No the sun is not shining today.

3. Yes I liked the movie.

4. No you may not play outside.

5. Yes the children have eaten lunch.

6. Yes the boys won the game.

7. No my mother is not here.

8. Yes it is snowing.

9. No I do not like cold weather.

10. Yes the girls are at the library.

11. Yes this is the lost book.

12. No he is not a fast runner.

13. Yes she works at the school.

14. No it didn't rain last night.

15. Yes our family is leaving on vacation tomorrow.

NAME_____ DATE_____

TEST

PART A Write three sentences beginning with *yes* and three sentences beginning with *no*. Put in the needed punctuation marks.

1. _____

2. _____

3. _____

4. _____

5. _____

6. _____

PART B Read each sentence. Put in the missing punctuation marks.

1. Yes I can go to the beach with you.

2. No you may not sleep in the tent tonight.

3. No our teacher is not here today.

4. Yes I saw the bears and tigers at the circus.

5 Yes Bill knows how to ride a horse.

6. No the doorbell is not working.

7. No I did not find my jacket.

8. Yes they saw the bank robbery happen.

9. No Doris does not like scary movies.

10. Yes our neighbors are nice people.

NAME _____ DATE_____

Read each sentence. Put in the missing punctuation marks. The first one has been done for you.

1. "Who is at the door?" called Sarah.

2. When do you have to go home? asked Mark.

3. June said, There are a lot of stars in the sky tonight.

4. The girl murmured, I lost my sweater.

5. We won the ball game, the girls hollered.

6. Father yelled, Don't play in the street.

7. The teacher questioned, How do you spell *basket*?

8. Mother inquired, Why are you late?

9. Paul replied, I forgot the time.

10. I got a new dog, said Laura.

11. What color is it? asked Carol.

12. It is sandy brown, replied Laura.

13. What kind of dog is it? questioned Beth.

14. It is a cocker spaniel, said Laura.

NAME_____ DATE_____

Read each sentence. Put in the quotation marks *only* when they are needed.

1. It is a beautiful day, said Mrs. Smith.

2. Where are my blue socks?

3. Jill said, It is almost time to go home.

4. Jim said that he could not go with us.

5. May we go to the movies? asked Mark.

6. Father replied, Yes, you may go.

7. Who turned off the lights?

8. The teacher said, Do not lie to me.

9. Where are you going on vacation? inquired Mrs. Johnson.

10. Sally shouted, What are you doing?

11. Did you turn off the lights?

12. The officer questioned, Why were you speeding?

NAME_____ DATE_____

Look at the sentences in PART A. Copy the punctuation marks into the appropriate places in PART B.

PART A:

1. "Did you see the new teachers?" asked Sam.

2. The man yelled, "Move out of the way."

3. "I am going over to Mrs. Brown's house," said Mother.

4. The children called, "Who's out there?"

5. "Where is my new sweater?" inquired Phil.

6. "We are going to eat supper soon," said Mother.

7. Mary groaned, "I can't find my report."

8. Father called, "Let's go ice skating."

PART B:

1. Did you see the new teacher? asked Sam.

2. The man yelled, Move out of the way.

3. I am going over to Mrs. Brown's house, said Mother.

4. The children called, "Who's out there?

5. Where is my new sweater? inquired Phil.

6. We are going to eat supper soon, said Mother.

7. Mary groaned, I can't find my report.

8. Father called, Let's go ice skating.

NAME_____ DATE_____

Read this short play. Rewrite each line as a sentence with quotation marks.

Jane: Have you seen my blue dress?

Mother: I sent it to the cleaners.

Jane: I wanted to wear it to the party tonight.

Mother: Bill, would you pick up Jane's dress at the cleaners on your way home?

Bill: Sure, I would be glad to.

Jane: Thank you, Bill and mother.

_____

_____

_____

_____

_____

_____

_____

_____

NAME_____ DATE_____

TEST

Read each sentence. Put in the missing quotation marks only where needed.

1. We are having tacos for supper, said Mother.

2. Who drew this picture? inquired the teacher.

3. There was a beautiful sunset tonight.

4. The principal questioned, Why were you fighting?

5. Les groaned, I hurt my foot.

6. I read a good book, said Beth.

7. Mr. and Mrs. Groves are on vacation.

8. The teacher said that we could play games now.

9. Will you help me? called Sandy.

10. Father answered, I'll be right there.

11. The man shouted, Watch out for the falling branch.

12. You should not ride your bike in the middle of the street, said the policeman.

13. We bought a new lamp.

14. Please turn the fan on, said Kathy.

15. They watched a funny program on the television.

NAME_____ DATE_____

Read each sentence. Put in the missing commas. The first one has been done for you.

1. Bess asked ,"Who is that lady?"

2. "Father is at work now" said Bob.

3. Carol exclaimed "I got an A on the test."

4. Dick repeated "Let's go this way."

5. "It's raining" groaned Jill.

6. "This is really a good basketball game" said Mark.

7. Father asked "Who wants to go for a walk?"

8. "I do" replied Wendy.

9. Betty inquired "Are you going to the library now?"

10. Carl repeated "I don't know the answer."

11. The principal questioned "Where did you find the matches?"

12. "We are going to the museum today" said Ned.

NAME_____ DATE_____

Read each sentence. Some of the quoted sentences need commas and some do not. If it needs a comma, put it in and write *yes* on the line. If it does not need a comma, write *no* on the line.

1. "What shall I do?" asked Steve. _____

2. "I don't know" said Tom. _____

3. "My car brakes don't work!" exclaimed Dad. _____

4. Mother said "Please clean your room." _____

5. "Do I have to do it now?" asked Mark. _____

6. "Yes, you do " said Mother. _____

7. Joan yelled "Watch where you're going!" _____

8. Mary groaned "I forgot to study for my test." _____

9. Peggy said "I'll help you study now." _____

10. "Did you eat your breakfast?" questioned Mom. _____

11. "Our soccer team is in first place!" shouted Paul. _____

12. Carol asked "Do you want to go swimming?" _____

NAME_____ DATE_____

TEST

Read each sentence. Some of the quoted sentences need commas and some do not. Put in the commas *only where needed*.

1. "Did you find your sweater?" asked Mom.

2. "Yes, I found it" said Linda.

3. "I forgot to do my book report" groaned Alan.

4. "That house is on fire!" yelled Mr. Nelson.

5. "When is the meeting?" asked the teacher.

6. Sam said "I don't feel well."

7. Mom shouted "Stay in the backyard!"

8. "Did you see the parade?" questioned Sandy.

9. Brian answered "No, we were gone."

10. The children said "We are going on a bus trip."

11. "My car won't start" groaned Jane.

12. Dad said "It is too cold today to play golf."

13. Mike groaned "We lost the game by one point."

14. "Have you seen my new watch?" inquired Karen.

15. "We are going for a hike" said Fred.

NAME_____ DATE_____

Read each sentence. Put in the missing exclamation point. The first one has been done for you.

1. It's snowing outside!

2. Watch where you're going

3. We won the game by one point

4. She's hurt

5. Don't play in the street

6. There's a fire in that building

7. That tree is falling

8. Keep out

9. I love America

10. My dog had puppies

11. I broke my leg

12. School's out for the summer

NAME_____ DATE_____

Read each sentence. Put in the missing punctuation mark. Then write one of the
following words on each line to describe the feeling for each sentence: *happy, sad,
mad, scared*. The first one has been done for you.

1. That's a big dog! *scared* _____

2. We lost the game _____

3. We won the game _____

4. I lost my new baseball _____

5. He took my last cookie _____

6. I don't have my homework _____

7. Quiet down, class _____

8. I got a new bike _____

9. It's starting to snow _____

10. Our dog is lost _____

11. We are moving to a new house_____

12. I don't feel good _____

NAME_____ DATE_____

TEST

Read each sentence. Put in the correct ending punctuation mark—period, question mark or exclamation point.

1. That house is on fire

2. What time is it

3. We bought a new car

4. Our new dog is brown and white

5. The boat is sinking

6. How much does that cost

7. Would you set the table for dinner

8. Please put your books away

9. Don't play in the mud

10. We won the soccer game

11. Are you coming over for dinner

12. Is it time to go to the movies

13. I am going to the library

14. It is a nice day

15. That bird is hurt

NAME_____ DATE_____

Read each sentence. Put in the missing punctuation marks — period, question mark or exclamation point. Then indicate what kind of sentence each one is by using this code: *Statement* = S, *Question* = Q, and *Exclamation* = E. The first one has been done for you.

1. Help me, please! __E_____

2. Where are the cookies _____

3. He is reading a book _____

4. Will you sing a song _____

5. Today is Karen's birthday _____

6. I lost all my money _____

7. That car is on fire _____

8. It is time to go to bed _____

9. Did you do your book report _____

10. Have you done your chores _____

11. We are going to Disneyland_____

12. What time is the meeting _____

13. Who is at the door _____

14. Did you water the plants _____

15. We lost the game _____

CAPITALIZATION/PUNCTUATION

NAME_____ DATE_____

Read each sentence. On the line following each sentence, indicate why the comma or commas are in that sentence. Use this code:

Comma — Date = D   Comma — City/State = C
Comma — Series = S   Comma — Quotation = Q
                Comma — Yes/No = Y/N

The first one has been done for you.

1. I bought a new blouse, dress, and skirt. ____S____

2. He lives in Dallas, Texas., _____

3. Father said, "I have to work late tonight." _____

4. She was born on May 23, 1977. _____

5. No, the bell has not rung yet. _____

6. Yes, the game is over. _____

7. Have you ever been to Omaha, Nebraska? _____

8. Paul exclaimed, "I forgot my lunch!" _____

9. They were married on November 20, 1980. _____

10. He played baseball, rode his bike, and did his homework. _____

11. They are going on vacation to Miami, Florida. _____

12. No, I don't know where Sam is. _____

13. "Here are the maps you wanted," said Mary. _____

14. Mother bought oranges, potatoes, milk, cookies, meat, and juice at the store.

_____

15. The baby was born on January 12, 1981. _____

NAME_____ DATE_____

Read each sentence. Circle the word that needs a capital letter in each sentence. Write the circled word on the line with the correct capital letter. The first one has been done for you.

1. The teacher asked, "(where) is Tom?" _Where_

2. "may I go to the party?" asked Mary. _____

3. "what a pretty day," said Mother. _____

4. The policeman hollered, "stay out of the street!" _____

5. Bill pleaded, "may I have more cake?" _____

6. Susan grumbled, "i can't go to the party." _____

7. Tom exclaimed, "we won the races!" _____

8. "where are the children playing?" inquired Father. _____

9. "what's the weather like today?" questioned Karen. _____

10. Mother replied, "it's a beautiful day." _____

11. "i can't do this work," repeated Mark. _____

12. The boy said, "our team plays very well. _____

NAME_____ DATE_____

Read each sentence. There is a punctuation mark missing in each sentence. Circle the word below each sentence which tells what punctuation mark is missing, and then put in the needed punctuation mark. The first one has been done for you.

1. There is no school today.

    question mark   (period)   comma

2. What time do you have to leave

    comma   period   question mark

3. My grandparents live in Memphis Tennessee.

    period   apostrophe   comma

4. No I can't go now.

    comma   period   exclamation point

5. We're winning the game

    exclamation point   question mark   comma

6. This is not my lunch, said Bob.

    period   comma   quotation marks

7. Mother bought a dress blouse and skirt at the store.

    period   apostrophe   comma

8. "There are no more cookies" said Sandra.

    quotation marks   period   comma

9. Paul was born on April 23 1972.

    exclamation point   comma   question mark

10. We cant finish the picture now.

    comma   period   apostrophe

NAME_____ DATE_____

TEST

Read each sentence. Put in the missing punctuation marks — quotation marks, commas or exclamation points.

1. Move out of the way

2. Yes it is Sunday.

3. They played baseball basketball volleyball and tag.

4. How old are you? asked Don.

5. Ken said "I'm hungry."

6. I found my book report

7. Bill Jane Karen and Carl are absent today.

8. What do you want for lunch? asked Mom.

9. No the boys have not finished their ball game.

10. Doris groaned "My tooth hurts."

11. "There are no more apples" said Beth.

12. I had eggs bacon toast juice and milk for breakfast.

13. Stay out of the street

14. Where is my bike? inquired Stan.

15. Yes I drew this picture.

OVERVIEW

A. **CAPITALIZATION**—More proper nouns (1. countries, peoples, continents; 2. bodies of water—rivers, lakes, oceans; 3. parks, mountains, special places, landmarks).

1. **Introduction**—Write the sentences on the chalkboard with proper nouns from group one (countries, peoples, continents) in them. Put the capital letter in with a different color chalk. Discuss the need for the capitals. Have the students copy sentences onto their paper.

   Sentences:

   a. We have visited Canada and Mexico.

   b. The United States is a part of North America.

   c. We are called Americans.

   d. They have gone on vacation to England and France.

   e. People born in Spain are called Spanish.

   f. Africa is a big continent.

   g. They had Italian food for supper.

   h. Another continent is Australia.

2. Worksheet #100

3. Worksheet #101

4. **Activity**—"Grab Bag"—The teacher makes up at least 20 cards with all proper nouns (countries, peoples, continents) in lower-case letters. Some of the words should be just common nouns. When 20 word cards are used, there should be only four players. Each player takes a turn at drawing a card from the bag. The player tells whether the word should or should not be capitalized. If he is correct, he keeps the card; if he is incorrect, the card is put back into the bag. The game is concluded when all of the cards have been drawn. The winner is the player with the most cards.

5. Worksheet #102—TEST

6. **Introduction**—Write sentences on the chalkboard with proper nouns from group two (bodies of water—rivers, lakes, oceans) in them. Put the capital letter in with different color chalk. Discuss the need for capitals. Have the students copy sentences onto their paper.

Sentences:

a. The Mississippi River is very long.

b. Bill lives near Brown Lake.

c. Both the Atlantic Ocean and Pacific Ocean are very big.

d. Have you ever seen Lake Tahoe?

e. They live near the Gulf of Mexico.

f. He took a trip on the Colorado River.

7. Worksheet #103

8. Worksheet #104

9. Worksheet #105 — TEST

10. **Introduction** — Write sentences on the chalkboard with proper nouns from group three (parks, mountains, special places, landmarks) in them. Put the capital letters in with a different color chalk. Discuss the need for capitals. Have the students copy the sentences onto their paper.

Sentences:

a. The Mojave Desert is in California.

b. My grandparents are at Catskill Park.

c. The Catskill Mountains are in New York.

d. Have you ever been to the Statue of Liberty?

e. Many ships use the Panama Canal.

f. Our friends have gone to the Everglades.

11. Worksheet #106

12. **Boardwork** — Write these words on the chalkboard. Students are to write a sentence on their papers for each word.

a. White House

b. Yellowstone National Park

c. Rocky Mountains

d. Golden Gate Bridge

e. Sea World

f. Disneyland

g. Grand Canyon

h. Lincoln Memorial

13. Worksheet #107

14. Worksheet #108

15. Worksheet #109

16. Worksheet #110

17. Worksheet #111 — TEST

B. **PUNCTUATION — Comma to set off words of Direct Address**

1. **Introduction** — The teacher says the following sentence to the class (with a little longer than normal pause after the comma): "Susan, I want to go to the party with you." She writes the sentence on the chalkboard and puts the comma in with a different color chalk. Then, she explains that introductory words and words of direct address at the beginning of a sentence are set off from the remainder of the sentence by a comma. Other sentences are written on the chalkboard and the commas are put in these sentences in different colored chalk. Students are to copy these sentences on their paper.

   Sentences:

   a. Mother, when are you going to the store?

   b. Pat, I don't want to do that.

   c. Let me see your bike, Ben.

   d. Will you come, Mary?

   e. Mark, will you help me with this?

   f. Tell me, Jim, if you can go.

   g. I asked you, Karen, if it is raining.

   h. The bell is ringing, Sam.

2. Worksheet #112

3. **Boardwork** — Copy these sentences onto your paper. Put in the missing commas.

   a. Dad the car is not working.

   b. I lost my keys Tom.

   c. Sit down Bob and be quiet.

   d. Mary finish your homework.

   e. Chris have you found your pen?

   f. Where is the ball game Bill?

   g. Call me Karen when you finish.

   h. This pen has no ink left Mom.

4. Worksheet #113

5. Worksheet #114 — TEST

C. **PUNCTUATION — Apostrophe in all forms of Possession**

1. **Introduction** — Write the words *boys' gloves, Gladys' dress,* and *dogs' houses* on the chalkboard. Explain that we put in the apostrophe after the *s* for possessives ending with *s*. Put several other groups of words on the

chalkboard. Have the students copy these groups of words onto their paper after discussion is completed on the apostrophe (including the exceptions).

Sentences:

a. girls' books

b. boys' hats

c. Charles' bike

d. clerks' paychecks

e. runners' shoes

f. horses' stable

g. teachers' cars

h. class' homework

i. men's coats

j. children's toys

2. Worksheet #115

3. Puzzles — The teacher should make up cards that have a word on one side and its possessive form on the other side. The teacher draws a jagged line on each card. These lines should vary from card to card with no two lines the same. The teacher writes a word on one side and on the other side of the card she writes its possessive form. The cards are cut along the line. Next, the puzzle pieces are mixed up and the students take turns matching the puzzle pieces. The students read each possessive and the word that it is made from after each match has been made.

4. Worksheet #116

5. Worksheet #117

6. Worksheet #118 — TEST

D. REVIEW

1. **Boardwork** — Put in the missing capital letters and punctuation marks.

Sentences:

a. Have you seen the rocky mountains?

b. Mark where are the car keys?

c. The horses blankets are in the stable.

d. I like to eat japanese food.

e. Where are the puppies toys?

f. Both europe and asia are continents.

g. Let me see your homework Carol.

h. We live in the united states of america.

2. Worksheet #119

3. **Boardwork**—Write a sentence for each group of words.

a. boys' bike

b. girls' dresses

c. runners' shoes

d. students' books

e. James' glove

f. babies' bottles

g. scouts' tents

h. farmers' tractors

4. Worksheet #120

5. Worksheet #121

6. Worksheet #122—TEST

CAPITALIZATION/PUNCTUATION WS#100

NAME _____ DATE_____

Read each sentence. Circle the words that need capital letters. Write the words correctly on the lines following each sentence. The first one has been done for you.

1. We had fun at the (mexican) party. _Mexican_ _____

2. They are going to visit europe this summer. _____

3. japan is a part of asia. _____ _____

4. We live in the united states. _____

5. I like chinese cookies. _____

6. Many people live in india. _____

7. Both north america and south america are continents. _____

_____

8. She has lived in brazil. _____

9. We had some good french pastry for breakfast. _____

10. Our friends are in germany, norway, and sweden for vacation. _____

_____

11. The continent of australia is not very big. _____

12. Do you like german potato salad? _____

141

NAME_____ DATE_____

In COLUMN ONE there are listed countries and continents. In COLUMN TWO there are the names of the peoples for the country or continent. On the line next to each item in COLUMNS ONE and TWO, write the words correctly with the needed capital letters. The first one has been done for you.

COLUMN ONE	COLUMN TWO
1. america *America*	1. american *American*
2. north american ____	2. north american ____
_____	_____
3. canada _____	3. canadian _____
4. mexico _____	4. mexican _____
5. france _____	5. french _____
6. japan _____	6. japanese _____
7. australia _____	7. australian _____
8. china _____	8. chinese _____
9. asia _____	9. asian _____
10. germany _____	10. german _____
11. england _____	11. english_____
12. ireland_____	12. irish_____
13. africa _____	13. african_____
14. russia _____	14. russian _____
15. europe_____	15. european_____

NAME_____ DATE_____

TEST

Read each sentence. Circle the words that need capital letters. Write the correct capital letter above the circled word. Then underline the word that tells why the word should be capitalized. The first one has been done for you.

1. Have you ever eaten any (greek) food?

   <u>peoples</u>   country   continent

2. africa is very big.

   peoples   country   continent

3. We went to a spanish party.

   peoples   country   continent

4. Germany and France are part of europe.

   peoples   country   continent

5. spain and sweden are a part of Europe.

   peoples   country   continent

6. south america and asia have many countries in them.

   peoples   country   continent

7. I like italian food.

   peoples   country   continent

8. Have you ever been to mexico?

   peoples   country   continent

9. Her grandparents moved here from norway.

   peoples   country   continent

10. scotland is next to ireland.

   peoples   country   continent

NAME_____ DATE_____

Read each sentence. Circle the words that need capital letters. Write the correct capital letter above each circled word. The first one has been done for you.

1. (lake erie) is by northern Ohio.

2. lake michigan is by Wisconsin and Michigan

3. lake superior is by northern Michigan.

4. lake huron is by eastern Michigan.

5. lake ontario is by northern New York.

6. You cross the pacific ocean to go to Hawaii.

7. You cross the atlantic ocean to go to England.

8. The sea of japan is between Japan and China.

9. The hudson bay is north of Ontario, Canada.

10. The arctic ocean is north of Asia.

11. The nile river is in Africa.

12. Have you seen the chesapeake bay?

13. The gulf of alaska is south of Alaska.

14. Where is the long island sound?

15. The arabian sea is east of India.

NAME_____ DATE_____

Read each group of words. Circle the letters that should be capital letters. Write the correct capital letters on the lines following each group of words. The first one has been done for you.

1. (C)hesapeake (B)ay _C_ _B_

2. black sea _____ _____

3. ohio river _____ _____

4. great salt lake _____ _____ _____

5. arctic ocean _____ _____

6. sea of japan _____ _____

7. long island sound _____ _____ _____

8. cape cod bay _____ _____ _____

9. pacific ocean _____ _____

10. baltic sea _____ _____

11. lake of the ozarks _____ _____

12. gulf of california _____ _____

13. nile river _____ _____

14. arabian sea _____ _____

15. danube river _____ _____

NAME _____ DATE_____

TEST

Read each sentence. Circle the words that need capital letters. Write the words with the needed capital letters on the line following each sentence. The first one has been done for you.

1. The (chesapeake bay) is between Maryland and Virginia. *Chesapeake Bay*

2. Have you ever seen any of the mississippi river? _____

3. Where is the great salt lake? _____

4. The adriatic sea is between Italy and Yugoslavia. _____

5. They vacationed near lake michigan. _____

6. Have you ever gone in the pacific ocean? _____

7. The hudson bay is north of Ontario, Canada. _____

8. The red sea is between Africa and Asia. _____

9. We took a trip on the missouri river. _____

10. The green bay is in Wisconsin _____

11. Are you going to lake tahoe this summer? _____

12. The nile river is in Egypt. _____

13. Where is the dead sea? _____

14. florida bay is by the tip of Florida. _____

15. They are going to visit friends at the lake of the ozarks. _____

NAME _____ DATE_____

Read each group of words. Capital letters are missing. Write the words on the lines correctly. The first one has been done for you.

1. sahara desert *Sahara Desert* _____

2. pike's peak _____

3. everglades national park _____

4. blue ridge mountains_____

5. independence hall _____

6. disneyland _____

7. death valley _____

8. big bend national park _____

   _____

9. san gabriel mountains _____

10. suez canal _____

11. mt. everest _____

12. olympic national park _____

13. mojave desert_____

14. garden of the gods _____

NAME_____ DATE_____

Read each sentence. There are capital letters missing in each sentence. Cross out the small letters and put the correct capital letters above them. The first one has been done for you.

1. They used to live in Spain and France.

2. Both europe and africa are continents.

3. We are going to see plymouth rock.

4. John took a boat trip on the hudson river.

5. The indian ocean is between africa and australia.

6. I am going fishing at cooper lake.

7. The picnic will be at washington park.

8. We bought some chinese fortune cookies.

9. Have you ever visited mexico?

10. The country of brazil is found in south america.

11. They are staying at lake tahoe.

12. The missouri river is big.

13. That dress has french lace on it.

14. We went to see niagara falls on our trip.

15. I have lived near the atlantic ocean.

16. Our friends live near the appalachian mountains.

NAME_____ DATE_____

Each word listed below is a country, continent, ocean, lake, river, landmark, park, mountains, or a people's nationality. Rewrite each word on the line next to it putting in the missing capital letters.

1. pacific ocean _____

2. atlantic ocean_____

3. europe_____

4. africa _____

5. asia _____

6. argentina _____

7. canada _____

8. new zealand _____

9. russia _____

10. grand canyon_____

11. niagara falls _____

12. lake michigan_____

13. hudson river _____

14. mississippi river_____

15. french _____

16. mexican _____

17. lincoln park _____

18. grand canyon national park_____

19. rocky mountains _____

20. adirondack mountains _____

NAME_____ DATE_____

Read the words by each number. One word or group of words in each line needs to be capitalized. Circle the word or group of words and then write the correct capital letter or letters above them. The first one has been done for you.

1. baseball   chili   *C R* (colorado river)
2. mountain   lake   smoky mountains
3. english   maps   plants
4. catskill park   taxi   river
5. land   europe   bus
6. country   towns   norway
7. blue ridge mountains streams   hills
8. parks   caribbean sea   seas
9. painted desert   city   ocean
10. chairs   hot dogs   st. lawrence river
11. lake superior   leader   strait
12. australia   books   continent
13. plane   peace   danish
14. japan   ivory   wars
15. states   cherries   yellowstone park

NAME _____ DATE_____

Read each sentence. Fill in the blanks with words from the Word Bank.

1. __ __ __ __ __ __ __ __ __ __ __ __ is a special landmark in South Dakota.

2. The __ __ __ __ __ __ __ Ocean is by California.

3. The __ __ __ __ __ Mountains are very big.

4. Have you ever seen Lake __ __ __ __ __ __ __ __?

5. The __ __ __ __ __ __ River is in New York.

6. They are going to __ __ __ __ __ __ __ __ __ __ for vacation.

7. The __ __ __ __ __ __ Desert is in Africa.

8. __ __ __ __ __ __ __ __ __ is a continent.

9. Her grandparents moved here from __ __ __ __ __ __ __.

10. People who come from Spain are called __ __ __ __ __ __ __.

11. Our class is going to visit __ __ __ __ __ __ __ __ __ __ __ __ __ __ __.

12. They moved here from __ __ __ __ __ __.

WORD BANK

Australia	Mount Rushmore	Finland
Pacific	Spanish	Rocky
Superior	Independence Hall	Hudson
Canada	Disneyland	Sahara

NAME _____ DATE _____

TEST

Read each sentence. The underlined word or words are capitalized for a reason. Write one of these words on the line following the sentence to tell why the underlined word or words is capitalized: country, continent, ocean, lake, river, mountains, park, peoples, and landmark. The first one has been done for you.

1. We lived near the <u>Hudson River</u>. _river_____

2. Mr. and Mrs. Jones went to <u>Holland</u>. _____

3. The baseball game will be at <u>Lincoln Park</u>. _____

4. Have you been to <u>Lake Tahoe</u>? _____

5. I like <u>Italian</u> food. _____

6. The <u>Rocky Mountains</u> are huge. _____

7. The <u>Pacific Ocean</u> is near us. _____

8. Canada is part of <u>North America</u>. _____

9. They are going to vacation near the <u>Wisconsin River</u>. _____

10. Did you go to <u>Everglades National Park</u>? _____

11. They are living in <u>Brazil</u>. _____

12. Our family is going to see the <u>Painted Desert</u>. _____

13. Bob and Mark are hiking in the <u>Catskill Mountains</u>. _____

14. They have gone to <u>Europe</u>. _____

15. The <u>Mississippi River</u> is very big. _____

NAME_____ DATE_____

Read each sentence. Put in the missing commas where needed. The first one has been done for you.

1. Scott, please put the dog outside

2. Have you seen my books Kathy?

3. Be quiet Tom or you'll stay after school.

4. Will you lend me a pencil Rick?

5. Jill is that your new dress?

6. Did you study for the test Jack?

7. I asked you Tom are you ready to play?

8. Pat did you win the game?

9. How do you do this Fred?

10. That is a good book Barb.

11. Sit down Doris and do your work.

12. What is the right answer Curt?

13. Paul it is time to go home.

14. This is my new football George.

15. Sally why were you absent yesterday?

NAME_____ DATE_____

Read the sentences. Rewrite the sentences putting in the missing commas.

1. Bill did you bring your math book?

   _____

2. Carol are you going home now?

   _____

3. Here is your lunch Todd.

   _____

4. Sit down Mark and do your work.

   _____

5. Jill what time is the party?

   _____

6. Write a paragraph Paula about your trip.

   _____

7. Anne this is a good picture.

   _____

8. Where are the boys playing ball Bob?

   _____

9. Is it going to be hot today Mother?

   _____

10. Les please open the door.

    _____

NAME _____ DATE_____

TEST

Read each sentence. Some of the sentences need commas and some do not. Put them in only where needed.

1. I told you Carl to get to work.

2. Mother where is my library book?

3. I have no paper.

4. Do you have a new dress Sharon?

5. What have you done with my lunch?

6. This is a beautiful day.

7. Be careful Paul with those dishes.

8. Linda where is my notebook?

9. The children are in the park Mom.

10. Dean are you going to the party?

11. Today is his birthday.

12. Write five sentences Nancy about your hobby.

13. There is no school tomorrow Dad.

14. Joe how many pencils do you need?

15. She was late for school.

NAME_____ DATE_____

Read each word. On the line next to each word, write the possessive for it. The first one has been done for you.

1. students *students'*_____

2. Frances _____

3. lions _____

4. bells _____

5. scouts _____

6. sailors _____

7. mothers _____

8. fathers _____

9. cats _____

10. girls _____

11. Thomas _____

12. puppies _____

13. pencils _____

14. friends _____

15. class _____

NAME_____ DATE_____

Read each sentence. Rewrite each sentence putting in the missing apostrophe.

1. Several of the farmers tractors are broken.

2. Thomas bike is red.

3. These pencils erasers are all used up.

4. The teachers lunches are not finished.

5. The scouts tents are all put up.

6. The class homework is not done yet.

7. My sisters rooms are neat and clean.

8. Have you seen James baseball?

9. Where are the runners prizes?

10. This is Gladys new dress.

NAME_____ DATE_____

Find the possessive word in COLUMN B for each word listed in COLUMN A. Put the number of the word from COLUMN A by the correct possessive form in COLUMN B.

COLUMN A	COLUMN B
1. brothers	____ farmers'
2. leaders	____ tigers'
3. families	____ clerks'
4. kittens	____ friends'
5. clerks	____ Gladys'
6. runners	____ families'
7. farmers	____ James'
8. winners	____ scouts'
9. tigers	____ brothers'
10. friends	____ teachers'
11. Gladys	____ winners'
12. scouts	____ leaders'
13. James	____ miners'
14. teachers	____ kittens'
15. miners	____ runners'

NAME_____ DATE_____

TEST

Read each sentence. On the line write the possessive form for each word. The first one has been done for you.

1. Our 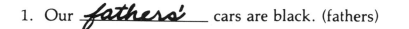 *fathers'* cars are black. (fathers)

2. The _____ meeting is tomorrow. (doctors)

3. The _____ erasers are broken. (pencils)

4. _____ bike has a flat tire. (James)

5. They found three _____ baseball caps. (boys)

6. Is this _____ house? (Charles)

7. The _____ bones are under the porch. (dogs)

8. My _____ bedrooms are very clean. (sisters)

9. The _____ rattles are in the playpen. (babies)

10. _____ tennis shoes are in his locker. (Thomas)

11. The _____ homework is on the chalkboard. (class)

12. The _____ robes are in that room. (singers)

13. The _____ boats are at the dock. (captains)

14. The _____ pages are torn. (books)

15. These _____ groups meet at the school. (ladies)

NAME_____ DATE_____

Read each sentence. The underlined word or words in each sentence are capitalized because they are proper nouns. On the line following the sentence write what kind of proper noun each is — country, continent, peoples, body of water, park, mountains, special place. The first one has been done for you.

1. They live near the <u>Blue Ridge Mountains</u>. *mountains*

2. Our neighbors are on vacation in <u>South America</u>. _____

3. The <u>Missouri River</u> joins the <u>Mississippi River</u>._____

4. I have visited <u>Canada</u> and <u>Mexico</u>. _____

5. His class took a trip to see the <u>Lincoln Memorial</u>. _____

6. Her blouse has <u>French</u> lace on it. _____

7. Have you seen the <u>Pacific Ocean</u>? _____

8. We vacationed at the <u>Everglades National Park</u>. _____

9. The girls went swimming at <u>West Lake</u>. _____

10. The picnic will be at <u>Lincoln Park</u>. _____

11. The <u>Rocky Mountains</u> are huge. _____

12. Our friends went to <u>Niagara Falls</u>. _____

13. They have never been to <u>Europe</u>. _____

14. Where is <u>Brazil</u> located? _____

15. His family took a trip on the <u>Ohio River</u>. _____

NAME_____ DATE_____

Read each group of words. Rewrite the continent and some of its countries with capital letters.

A. north america_____ _____

   1. united states _____ _____

   2. canada _____

   3. mexico _____

B. south america_____ _____

   1. brazil _____

   2. argentina_____

   3. chile _____

   4. uruguay_____

   5. venezuela _____

   6. colombia _____

   7. peru _____

C. europe_____

   1. germany _____

   2. sweden _____

   3. norway _____

   4. belgium _____

   5. france_____

   6. italy _____

   7. spain _____

   8. england _____

D. asia _____

   1. japan _____

   2. india _____

   3. korea_____

   4. viet nam _____

   5. thailand_____

   6. burma _____

   7. iraq _____

   8. syria _____

NAME_____ DATE_____

Read each sentence. Put in the missing comma or apostrophe where needed.

1. Mike which car is yours?

2. Stand still Paul and be quiet.

3. The captains catches of fish were good.

4. This is not my notebook Mrs. Carlson.

5. Several of the houses roofs have holes in them.

6. Thomas basketball is going flat.

7. Please shut the window Sally.

8. The mothers children are all at the skating rink.

9. Frances birthday is next week.

10. Mr. Jones son is your new boss.

11. All of the puppies eyes are open now.

12. Here are the eggs Mother.

CAPITALIZATION/PUNCTUATION

WS#122

NAME_____ DATE_____

TEST

Read each sentence. Put in the missing capital letters or punctuation marks.

1. The doctors cars are in the parking lot.

2. Mr. Jones is in greece.

3. They lived near the catskill mountains.

4. Paul what is the correct answer?

5. We are going to play ball at hillside park.

6. We are having spanish food for supper.

7. Sit down Ned and get to work.

8. Where is the indian ocean?

9. The mothers cakes are on the table.

10. Our neighbors are going to see the hoover dam and the grand canyon.

11. Have you ever been to france and italy in europe?

12. Let me see your new bike Jenny.

13. We went to lake tahoe for the week-end.

14. Gladys dress has a rip in it.

15. The boys are camping near the hudson river.

OVERVIEW

A. **CAPITALIZATION**—**Review of all rules previously taught.**

1. **Boardwork**—Copy these sentences. Put in the missing capital letters.

    Sentences:

    a. today is _____ _____ _____.
    b. where did i put my jacket?
    c. bill and john are playing ball.
    d. we celebrate halloween in october.
    e. carol said, "there is going to be a party."
    f. we went to dallas, texas for easter vacation.
    g. his boss is president jones.
    h. the grand canyon is large.

2. Worksheet #123

3. Worksheet #124

4. Worksheet #125

5. **Activity**—"Grab Bag"—The teacher makes up at least 20 work cards with all lower-case letters. Some of the words should be proper nouns. Each player takes a turn at drawing a card from the bag. The player tells whether the word should or should not be capitalized. If he is correct, he keeps the card; if he is incorrect, the card is put back into the bag. The game is concluded when all of the cards have been drawn. The winner is the player with the most cards.

6. Worksheet #126

7. Worksheet #127

8. **Activity**—Bulletin Board—The teacher puts this title at the top of the bulletin board, "Uses of Capital Letters." Underneath this, she puts one of the long strips. Each strip is to have a different rule written on it (i.e., first word of a sentence, titles, people's names, days, etc.). The teacher puts up the strip for the rule that the class is presently studying. Below the strip she puts up a sheet of the white paper—lengthwise. She writes a sentence that utilizes the rule (i.e., for First Word of a Sentence, she might write "The sun is shining."). The

capital letter at the beginning of the sentence should be written with the different color marker while the remainder of the sentence is written in black. Then, the students can write different sentences on this paper in the same manner. The paper can be changed when it is full, and the strip for that rule can be left up for as long as the teacher wants to have the students practice that rule. As the class moves on to other capitalization rules, the teacher should change the strip to the rule that is being emphasized or reviewed. The same procedure should be followed for the other rules.

9. Worksheet #128 — TEST

B. PUNCTUATION — **Review of all rules previously taught.**

1. **Boardwork** — Copy these sentences. Put in the missing punctuation marks.

   Sentences:
   a. Today is a nice day
   b. Where are my shoes
   c. Tomorrow will be _____ _____ _____
   d. Dr and Mrs Clark are at the theatre
   e. They live on Blackburn Ave in town
   f. We can't go to the party
   g. I bought a blouse skirt dress and jacket
   h. Mother said Dont play in the street

2. Worksheet #129

3. Worksheet #130

4. Worksheet #131

5. **Boardwork** — Students are to copy each word onto their paper. Then, they are to write the abbreviation next to each word that can be abbreviated.

a. New York	f. Mother	k. Mister
b. October	g. Reverend	l. May
c. Tuesday	h. California	m. Road
d. June	i. Monday	n. Texas
e. Avenue	j. January	o. Saturday

6. Worksheet #132

7. Worksheet #133

8. **Activity** — "Puzzles" — See previous levels where the puzzles were made up for contractions and possessives.

9. Worksheet #134

10. Worksheet #135 — TEST

C. REVIEW

1. Worksheet #136 — Review Capital Letters

2. Worksheet #137 — Review Punctuation Marks

3. Worksheet #138 — TEST

NAME_____ DATE_____

PART A   Follow each direction. Remember to use capital letters as needed.

1. My full name is _____

2. My friend's name is _____

3. My teacher's name is _____

4. My mother's name is _____

5. My father's name is _____

6. Write the name of a pet here_____

7. The name of my school is _____

8. I live in the city of _____

9. I live in the state of _____

10. I live in the country of _____

PART B   Write each name correctly.

1.   edward _____   6. lynn _____

2.   robert _____   7. donna _____

3.   james_____   8. jane _____

4.   charles _____   9. kathy_____

5.   paul _____   10. mary ann _____

NAME_____ DATE_____

Read each group of words. One word or group of words needs a capital letter or letters. Cross out the small letter(s) and put in the correct capital(s). The first one has been done for you.

1. ~~W~~illiam	chair	sink
2. pet	desk	rover
3. furnace	book	february
4. hamburger	wednesday	apple
5. film	company	memorial day
6. street	paper	peck road
7. chicago	plant	dessert
8. party	radio	montana
9. curtains	lincoln school	movie
10. england	sofa	pool
11. horse	blanket	atlantic ocean
12. africa	city	pencil
13. dress	pot	missouri river
14. heart	brown lake	window
15. bed	box	rocky mountains
16. cooper park	river	girl
17. glass	mirror	painted desert
18. spanish	ham	peanuts
19. cup	college	harvard university
20. muffins	jennifer	clock

NAME_____ DATE_____

Words that name peoples or items from a country or continent begin with capital letters. Read each country or continent and the word for the peoples that is on the line
next to it. Cross out the small letter and write the correct capital letter above it. The
first one has been done for you.

1.	America	*A*merican	16.	Africa	african
2.	Canada	canadian	17.	Australia	australian
3.	Mexico	mexican	18.	Brazil	brazilian
4.	England	english	19.	Russia	russian
5.	France	french	20.	Belgium	belgian
6.	Spain	spanish	21.	Poland	polish
7.	Italy	italian	22.	Portugal	portugese
8.	Denmark	danish	23.	Greece	Greek
9.	Norway	norwegian	24.	Cuba	cuban
10.	Sweden	swedish	25.	Ireland	irish
11.	Germany	german	26.	Scotland	scottish
12.	China	chinese	27.	Ethiopia	ethiopian
13.	Japan	japanese	28.	Egypt	egyptian
14.	India	indian	29.	Malaysia	malaysian
15.	Asia	asian	30.	Switzerland	swiss

NAME_____ DATE_____

Read each sentence. Circle the words that need capital letters. Write the whole word with the needed capital letter above the circled word. The first one has been done for you.

1. Both *North America* and *South America* are continents.

2. john, ruth, karen and mark are absent today.

3. mother said that i may go with you.

4. They go to carver high school.

5. My sister is attending wilson college.

6. We do not have school in july and august.

7. Two of the holidays are memorial day and labor day.

8. mr. and mrs. johnson are in new orleans, louisiana.

9. Our new horse is called fury.

10. Are you going shopping on thursday or friday?

11. Bill yelled, "let's play ball."

12. His name is dr. r. moore.

13. Our dentist's office is on washington boulevard.

14. The country of denmark is found on the continent of europe.

15. They took a trip down the mississippi river.

16. The picnic will be at grover park.

17. I have lived near the blue ridge mountains and the pacific ocean.

18. Both italian and french food were served at the banquet.

19. Our class is taking a trip to niagara falls.

20. rev. and mrs. wilson went on vacation to blue lake.

NAME_____ DATE_____

Read each sentence. Write the words which are capitalized under the correct rule listed at the bottom of this paper. The first one has been done for you.

1. I have lived in California, Colorado, and Maine.

2. My favorite holidays are Christmas and Easter.

3. The twins' names are John and Jean.

4. Mr. Cooper, Mrs. Smith, and Dr. Horn are at a meeting.

5. Have you ever visited Asia?

6. They attend Jefferson School.

7. We live near the Colorado River.

8. The Indian Ocean is near India.

9. Our neighbors are staying at Lake Tahoe.

10. There is no school on Saturday and Sunday.

River, Ocean or Lake	Country/ Continent	Abbreviation	School

First Word of Sentence	Proper Name	City/ State	Day, Month, or Holiday
I		California Colorado Maine	

NAME_____ DATE_____

TEST

Read each sentence. The underlined word in each sentence is capitalized because of one of the rules listed below. Please put the letter of the correct rule on the line following each sentence. The first one has been done for you.

a.	First word of sentence	f.	City or State
b.	Month or Day	g.	Country or Continent
c.	Proper name	h.	Special Place/Landmark
d.	Holiday	i.	Body of Water
e.	Abbreviations or Initials	j.	Street, Road, Boulevard, etc.

1. She was born on <u>December</u> 8th. __*b*_____

2. They visited <u>Old Faithful</u>. _____

3. <u>Mr.</u> and <u>Mrs.</u> Martin live next door. _____

4. Has <u>Donna</u> gone to work? _____

5. We live in the <u>United States</u>. _____

6. <u>Where</u> is the ball game being played? _____

7. He has moved to <u>Cooper Road</u>. _____

8. They flew across the <u>Pacific Ocean</u>. _____

9. His birthday is on <u>Valentine's Day</u>. _____

10. Our neighbors moved to <u>Atlanta, Georgia</u>. _____

11. <u>The</u> men are fixing the roof. _____

12. Have you ever been to <u>Australia</u>? _____

13. Our class went to see the <u>Washington Monument</u>. _____

14. There is no school on <u>Labor Day</u>. _____

15. My parents went to <u>Blue Lake</u> for the week-end. _____

16. His name is <u>B. R.</u> Nelson. _____

17. I gave the book to <u>Carl</u>. _____

18. Our family visited <u>Dayton, Ohio</u>. _____

19. Their new office is on <u>Main Street</u>. _____

NAME _____ DATE_____

PART A Follow each direction. Remember the needed periods.

1. My initials are _____.

2. My teacher's initials are _____.

3. My father's initials are _____.

4. My mother's initials are _____.

5. My best friend's initials are _____.

6. Lisa Johnson's initials are _____.

7. Tom Robinson's initials are _____.

8. Paul Green's initials are _____.

9. Mary Ruth Brown's initials are _____.

10. Steven Mark Miller's initials are _____.

PART B Put in the missing apostrophe for each possessive word.

1. Bobs car   6. Peters book

2. Carols sweater   7. Susans report

3. Jeans lunch   8. Lynns dress

4. Bens bike   9. Pauls ticket

5. Marks glove   10. Paulas purse

NAME_____ DATE_____

Read each word in COLUMN A. Find its lettered abbreviation in COLUMN B. On the line next to the abbreviation write the number of the word that it matches.

	COLUMN A		COLUMN B	
1.	February	a.	Wed.	_____
2.	Street	b.	Sept.	_____
3.	Mister	c.	Ave.	_____
4.	Wednesday	d.	Mon.	_____
5.	Avenue	e.	Rev.	_____
6.	Doctor	f.	Feb.	_____
7.	November	g.	Ct.	_____
8.	Monday	h.	Nov.	_____
9.	Friday	i.	Pl.	_____
10.	Boulevard	j.	Fri.	_____
11.	Miss	k.	St.	_____
12.	August	l.	Aug.	_____
13.	Place	m.	Blvd.	_____
14.	Reverend	n.	Dec.	_____
15.	Thursday	o.	Sun.	_____
16.	September	p.	Mr.	_____
17.	Road	q.	Thur.	_____
18.	Sunday	r.	Rd.	_____
19.	Court	s.	Dr.	_____
20.	December	t.	Miss	_____

NAME_____ DATE_____

Read each sentence. Put in the ending punctuation mark — period, question mark or exclamation point.

1. Is this a question

2. Look out for the falling branch

3. Please close the door

4. What do you like to do

5. What is her name

6. We are going out to dinner

7. Today is my birthday

8. We won the soccer game

9. Did you shut the windows

10. Where do you live

11. This is a funny t.v. show

12. Please help me

13. These boxes are heavy

14. It is time to eat lunch

15. Where is my book report

NAME_____ DATE_____

Each group of two words can be shortened and written as a contraction. Write the contraction for each group on the line next to the words. Remember the apostrophes. The first one has been done for you.

1. can not   _____can't_____

2. I will   _____

3. they are   _____

4. who is   _____

5. we would   _____

6. are not   _____

7. should not   _____

8. he is   _____

9. we are   _____

10. they would _____

11. have not   _____

12. it is   _____

13. they have   _____

14. what is   _____

15. you would   _____

16. we will   _____

17. she would   _____

18. would not   _____

19. I have   _____

20. do not   _____

NAME_____ DATE_____

Look at each word below. Rewrite the word to show possession by adding an apostrophe and an s or just an apostrophe. The first one has been done for you.

1. teacher   *teacher's*_____
2. Bob   _____
3. students   _____
4. Father   _____
5. Mother   _____
6. doctors   _____
7. James   _____
8. horses   _____
9. cat   _____
10. Mary   _____
11. Thomas   _____
12. Gladys   _____
13. George   _____
14. farmers   _____
15. captains   _____
16. dog   _____
17. sister   _____
18. kittens   _____
19. leaders   _____
20. scout   _____

NAME_____ DATE_____

Each sentence needs a comma or commas. Put in the commas where needed. Then use the code to indicate on the line following each sentence why the comma or commas are needed. The first one has been done for you.

Comma in Date = C/D
Commas between City and State = C/CS
Comma in a Series = C/S
Comma after Yes or No = C/YN
Comma in Quotations = C/Q
Comma in words of Direct Address = C/DA

1. He was born on September 7, 1980. _C/D_____

2. Mother bought meat bread eggs and milk. _____

3. No I cannot go with you. _____

4. They have moved to Tulsa Oklahoma. _____

5. Mary please bring me the scissors. _____

6. Jim asked "Do you have an extra pencil?" _____

7. The boys rode bikes played ball and played tag after school. _____

8. Sit down Mark and be quiet. _____

9. They saw the play on June 7 1981. _____

10. "I lost my jacket" said Marie. _____

11. Yes it is raining. _____

12. We are going to visit New York New York. _____

13. No the bell is not working. _____

14. Have you ever been to Philadelphia Pennsylvania? _____

15. I bought a notebook pencils erasers pens and paper for school. _____

16. Put the box over there Paul. _____

NAME_____ DATE_____

TEST

Read each sentence. Put in the missing punctuation marks — period, question mark, exclamation point, comma, apostrophe, and quotation marks.

1. Bill is not in school today

2. Where are the cookies

3. That building is on fire

4. Dr Cook Mr Jones and Mr Martin have gone to a meeting

5. Miss B L Carson has a new job

6. No you are not finished yet

7. Havent you found your pictures

8. Karen here is your lunch

9. Fathers car is not working

10. Our neighbors have gone to Las Vegas Nevada

11. It is going to be a nice day said Mom

12. Gladys dress is pretty

13. He is looking for his baseball glove baseball and cap

14. Her birthdate is March 19 1972

15. Rev and Mrs J Brown are the new pastors

NAME_____ DATE_____

Read each sentence. The underlined word in each sentence is capitalized for one of these reasons — first word of sentence, pronoun "I", names, month, day, holiday, street, city, state, school, title, initials, abbreviations, first word of quotation, country, continent, body of water, park, mountains, special place and peoples. On the lines following each sentence list one of the above rules to indicate why the underlined word is capitalized. The first one has been done for you.

1. Have you ever been to <u>Europe</u>? *name of a continent*

2. Mother said that <u>I</u> may go. _____

3. My favorite months are <u>July</u> and <u>August</u>. _____

4. Mom said, "<u>What</u> a pretty dress." _____

5. Our class is going to see the <u>Grand Canyon</u>. _____

6. Their new office is on <u>Park Avenue</u>. _____

7. I have a new cat named <u>Tabby</u>. _____

8. <u>Mr.</u> and <u>Mrs.</u> Clark are at the hospital. _____

9. He is working in <u>England</u>. _____

10. <u>Paul</u> and <u>Tom</u> have lost their bikes. _____

11. <u>Who</u> brought the chocolate cake? _____

12. They have gone to <u>Blue Lake</u>. _____

13. The picnic will be at <u>Wilson Park</u>. _____

14. My sister attends <u>Hoover High School</u>. _____

15. Lisa <u>M.</u> Cooper is my friend. _____

16. Have you ever seen the <u>Rocky Mountains</u>? _____

(continued)

17. The <u>Pacific Ocean</u> is huge. _____

18. Are you going to the library on <u>Monday</u> or <u>Tuesday</u>? _____

19. The head of the company is <u>President</u> Johnson. _____

20. Our friends went to <u>San Francisco</u>. _____

21. We are having <u>Spanish</u> food for supper. _____

22. Her birthday is on <u>Christmas Eve</u>. _____

23. The boys took a boat trip on the <u>Hudson River</u>. _____

24. They are moving to <u>Indiana</u>. _____

25. We live in <u>North America</u>. _____

26. <u>There</u> is no school today. _____

27. Our family once lived in <u>Chicago</u>. _____

28. The ball game is at <u>Lincoln Park</u>. _____

29. My birthday is in <u>November</u>. _____

30. I saw <u>John</u> at the party. _____

31. Do you like <u>Italian</u> food? _____

32. Bill asked, "<u>Where</u> are my brown shoes?" _____

33. We are going to grandmother's on <u>Easter</u>. _____

34. Have you been to <u>Niagara Falls</u>? _____

35. He attends <u>Harvard University</u>. _____

NAME_____ DATE_____

Look at the underlined words in each sentence. Put the correct punctuation mark before, after, or in each of these words.

1. Steves ball club is playing at the park on South Street

2. Mr Jones asked, Was the car green

3. Im going to the zoo on August 14 1982.

4. Did Mrs Smith give Johns coat to Sammy

5. The boat is sinking

6. Yes you passed the test

7. Gladys blouse has a tear in it.

8. Their friends have gone to Phoenix Arizona.

9. Dr P L Cooper is very nice.

10. Mom cleaned the bedrooms the bathrooms the den and the kitchen.

11. Who won the game

12. Have you seen my bike? asked Roger.

13. John here is your lunch ticket.

14. Mrs. Brown said "These are good cookies."

15. Watch out

NAME_____ DATE_____

TEST

Read each sentence. There are capital letters and punctuation marks missing. Put in the needed punctuation marks and cross out the small letters putting the needed capital letters above.

1. the sun is not shining today

2. what are the children playing

3. Our neighbors are visiting spain and france in europe

4. Mr and Mrs Cooper were married on june 23 1965

5. Thomas car wont start

6. i saw dr and mrs Cook at the restaurant

7. My friend lives in akron ohio

8. No i have never seen niagara falls

9. Rev G Wood is our new pastor

10. We won the game by one point

11. here are the papers you needed said Carol

12. bob tom carl and paul are playing tennis

13. Martha j Downs is a new girl at school

14. he lives on parker street

15. bevs new sweater is red and white.

16. we drove through the smoky mountains

17. The indian ocean is near india

18. Please bring me a cup kathy

19. the mississippi river is very long.

20. Bill asked where are the car keys

OVERVIEW
(Sentences)

A. STATEMENTS/Using a Period

1. **Introduction** — The teacher writes the words "The sky" on the chalkboard and asks the students what the words tell them. She leads them, if necessary, to the realization that the words actually tell nothing. The class then participates in adding words so that a group of words that tells something is written on the board. The teacher then explains that a group of words that tells something is a sentence that is called a statement and is followed by a period. She should place a colored period at the end of the statement and write the words "sentence" and "statement" on the chalkboard. Continue by writing other sentence fragments on the chalkboard for the class to complete. Let the students add the periods using colored chalk. Last, the students are to copy these complete statements onto their papers.

    Sentences:

    a. The big brown dog

    b. A small boy

    c. The sun

    d. The old woman

    e. A shiny apple

    f. The beautiful horse

    g. The broken toy

    h. Mr. Applegate

2. Worksheet #139

3. Worksheet #140

4. **Boardwork** — Write scrambled sentences on the chalkboard. The first word of the sentence is capitalized and the period is placed after the last word. Students are to copy the words in correct order to make sentences.

    a. to   Bob   store.   went   the

    b. likes   to   Dan   ball.   play

    c. basketball.   has   The   a   boy   new

    d. after   cat   mouse.   the   ran   The

    e. nice   Today   a   day.   is

f. yard.   rake   I   the   will

g. dog   The   away.   ran

h. shut   Please   the   door.

5. Worksheet #141

5. Worksheet #142

6. Worksheet #143 — TEST

B. **QUESTIONS/Using a Question Mark**

1. **Introduction:** The teacher makes a large question mark on the chalkboard in colored chalk, and says, "This is a question mark." She writes the words *question mark* next to the mark. Next, she writes the question, "What is Bill doing?" on the chalkboard. The question mark should be placed in colored chalk. Explain to the students why the question mark was used in the sentence. Write other questions on the chalkboard and have different students put colored question marks at the end of each sentence after they have been read. Finally, write the following paragraph on the chalkboard and have the students, as a class, read and punctuate it correctly.

   My dog ran away Monday   He is brown and white

   His name is Rags   Has anyone seen him

2. **Boardwork** — Copy each question. Put in the question mark.

   Sentences:

   a. What is that

   b. Who is making that noise

   c. Where do you live

   d. When will you be finished

   e. How far can you throw the ball

   f. Are you going to the park

   g. Why didn't you stay after school

   h. May I have a cookie

2. Worksheet #144

3. Worksheet #145

4. **Boardwork** — Write scrambled questions on the chalkboard. The first word of the sentence is capitalized and the question mark is placed after the last word of the question. Students copy the questions onto their papers in correct order.

Sentences:

a. that   Who   making   noise?   is

b. new   you   Did   a   game?   buy

c. cookies?   the   are   Where   chocolate

d. the   time   meeting?   is   What

e. ready   eat   you   dinner?   Are   to

f. go   a   for   like   ride?   you   Would   to

g. Does   his   Bill   have   homework   done?

h. you   game?   do   play   How   this

5. Worksheet #146

6. Worksheet #147 — TEST

C. **REVIEW: Statements/Questions**

1. **Boardwork:** Write sentences on the chalkboard. Students are to copy the sentences and put in the period or question mark.

    Sentences:

    a. It is snowing outside

    b. Today is a cold, windy day

    c. Do you like spaghetti

    d. Mother is a good cook

    e. Will you please be quiet

    f. Where is my pencil

    g. Is he finished reading the book

    h. They bought a new television

2. Worksheet #148

3. **Activity** — "What Is It?" — The teacher gives each student a paper strip that has a question or a statement on it. There is no period or question mark on these paper strips. Each student, in turn, reads his sentence aloud and tells whether it is a statement or a question. As an assignment, each student writes his sentence on the chalkboard with the correct punctuation mark. The students are to copy the sentences onto their papers.

4. **Boardwork** — Write statements or questions on the chalkboard. The students are to copy the sentences. They are to change the question to a statement or the statement to a question.

    Example: a.   She is a nice girl.
                           Is she a nice girl?

    b.   Are the boys playing football?
         The boys are playing football.

    c.   Has Jane walked her dog?

    d.   The children have gone to bed.

    e.   Did he park the car?

    f.   Mrs. Johnson is my teacher.

5.   Worksheet #149

6.   **Activity** — "Switch" — Use the paper strips that were made up for "What is It?". Each student receives a paper strip. He reads his sentence aloud and tells whether it is a statement or a question. He then changes it to a question if it is a statement or to a statement if it is a question.

7.   Worksheet #150

8.   Worksheet #151

9.   Worksheet #152

10. Worksheet #153 — TEST

NAME_____ DATE_____

Read each group of words. If it is a sentence, write *yes* on the line and put the period in. If it is not a sentence, write *no* on the line.

1. It is time to go home _____

2. I have a new bike _____

3. The juicy orange _____

4. Running very quickly _____

5. Up in the sky _____

6. The women are sewing a quilt _____

7. My favorite fruit is an orange _____

8. The ice cream sundae _____

9. I went to see the new movie _____

10. Coming down the street _____

11. That is a pretty plant_____

12. She bought a new painting _____

13. The new girl _____

14. The car raced down the road _____

15. Upside down _____

NAME_____ DATE_____

Read each group of words. If the words are a statement, put in the period. If the words are not a statement, add words to make a statement and put in the period.

1. Mrs. Martin

2. It is a lovely day

3. The children are on the playground

4. A big, red ball

5. The oak tree

6. My mother and father

7. We had pie for dessert

8. The boys played baseball

9. Our dog is very friendly

10. My brother

11. A little bird

12. The smashed car

13. They bought a new sofa and chair

14. Those are very pretty pictures

15. The big man

NAME_____ DATE_____

Write a sentence for each word.

1. dog

_____

2. house

_____

3. cowboy

_____

4. car

_____

5. chair

_____

6. talk

_____

7. run

_____

8. work

_____

9. jump

_____

10. yelled

_____

NAME_____ DATE_____

Arrange each group of words in order to make a sentence. Put in the period. The first
one has been done for you.

1. was   no   There   this   sun   morning

   There was no sun this morning.

2. wind   A   all   cold   blew   day

   _____

3. will   Soon   snow   it

   _____

4. saw   new   We   the   helicopter

   _____

5. store   went   Mother   the   to

   _____

6. not   clock   ticking   The   is

   _____

7. big   is   storm   coming   A

   _____

8. has   the   gone   to   She   doctor

   _____

9. was   the   car   speeding   The   road   down

   _____

10. beach   We   going   the   are   to

   _____

11. sister   away   is   My   moving

   _____

12. a   seeing   children   film   The   are

   _____

NAME_____ DATE_____

TEST

Read each group of words. Some of these are sentences and some are not. Add words to those groups that are not sentences to make a sentence. Put in the period for all the sentences.

1. The clock chimed the hour

2. Mr. and Mrs. Smith

3. Our television set

4. We watched a funny program on television

5. The little dog

6. The pretty girl

7. Father has gone to work

8. The airplane

9. He got a haircut

10. The boys ran in the race

11. The pink balloon

12. My friend

13. Our class is working on a project

14. Mother is doing the laundry

15. Those books

16. What a beautiful house

18. That big, old tree

19. A pretty rainbow

20. The tiny baby girl

NAME_____ DATE_____

Read each group of words. If the words make a question, write *yes* on the line and put in the question mark. If the words do not make a question, write *no* on the line.

1. When are you coming to my house _____

2. Seeing a pretty stone _____

3. Would you help me find my books _____

4. How old are you _____

5. The old television set _____

6. Why are you walking so fast _____

7. Have you seen my new dog _____

8. The beautiful flower _____

9. Smiling very nicely _____

10. Will you be able to finish that report _____

11. May I play at Jane's house _____

12. Sailing the big boat _____

13. Miss Adams and Mrs. Jones _____

14. Where are you moving to _____

15. Are you having a birthday party _____

NAME_____ DATE_____

Write a question that begins with each word listed below.

1. Who

_____

2. Is

_____

3. What

_____

4. Could

_____

5. Why

_____

6. Are

_____

7. How

_____

8. When

_____

9. Where

_____

10. Have

_____

NAME_____ DATE_____

Arrange each group of words in order to make a question. Put in the question mark. The first one has been done for you.

1. Did   find   football   you   your

   _Did you find your football?_____

2. parents   Where   your   are

   _____

3. dog   that   Is   barking   your

   _____

4. soon   have   go   How   do   to   you   home

   _____

5. put   toys   you   Would   your   away

   _____

6. jump   Can   rope   you

   _____

7. ball   outside   left   Who   the

   _____

8. fix   Will   man   roof   the   the

   _____

9. going   What   you   time   dinner   are   to

   _____

10. story   Are   listening   you   the   to

    _____

11. were   late   you   Why

    _____

12. more   need   you   Do   paper   any

    _____

NAME _____ DATE_____

TEST

Read each group of words. Some of these are questions and some are not. Add words to those groups that are not sentences to make questions. Put in the question mark for all the questions.

1. Where is

2. Who left the skates on the stairs

3. Will you

4. Would

5. Are you ready to go

6. What do you want me to do now

7. How can I help you

8. Who

9. Is the sun

10. Did you put the paints away

11. Who is working on this puzzle

12. Will the boys finish the race

13. Have the girls

14. Where are the crayons

15. When is

NAME_____ DATE_____

PART A Write a sentence for each word.

1. hotel

_____

2. teacher

_____

3. children

_____

4. walking

_____

5. eats

_____

PART B Write a sentence *beginning* with each word.

6. How

_____

7. Why

_____

8. Are

_____

9. Would

_____

10. What

_____

NAME_____ DATE_____

Read each sentence. Rewrite the statements (telling sentences) as questions (asking sentences). Rewrite the questions (asking sentences) as statements (telling sentences). The first one has been done for you.

1. Did the bell ring?

   *The bell did ring.*_____

2. Bill is at the park

   _____

3. The sun is shining today

   _____

4. Is it going to snow?

   _____

5. Does Barb like to eat ham?

   _____

6. Are we going to play ball?

   _____

7. That is a big house.

   _____

8. Is this Ken's homework paper?

   _____

9. Are Carl and Tom staying after school?

   _____

10. Has Peggy finished the book report?

    _____

NAME_____ DATE_____

Arrange each group of words in order so that they make a sentence. Put in the period or question mark at the end of the sentence. The first one has been done for you.

1. eggs   breakfast   We   bacon   and   for   had

   We had bacon and eggs for breakfast.

2. my   Have   seen   bike   you

   _____

3. school   to   do   go   What   you

   _____

4. tastes   That   good   cake

   _____

5. do   dishes   you   the   Did

   _____

6. baby   in   The   crib   the   is

   _____

7. our   company   have   We   home   at

   _____

8. asleep   you   aren't   Why

   _____

9. raking   backyard   Father   the   is

   _____

10. want   What   lunch   do   for   you

   _____

NAME _____ DATE_____

PART A   MAKING STATEMENTS
Copy the right part in each blank. Put a period after each statement.

a.   two little rabbits   d.   not want to work

b.   saw a pretty bird   e.   a good book

c.   fun this year   f.   listen to the teacher

1. She is reading_____

2. School is_____

3. You should_____

4. She bought_____

5. The boys do _____

6. The girl _____

PART B: MAKING QUESTIONS
Copy the right part in each blank. Put a question mark after each question.

a.   your bicycle   d.   the teacher go

b.   have a dog   e.   see it, please

c.   in that box   f.   stop raining soon

7. May I _____

8. Does John _____

9. Where did _____

10. Is that _____

11. What is _____

12. Will it _____

NAME_____ DATE_____

Read each question. Answer each question with a complete sentence.

1. What is your name?

   _____

2. How old are you?

   _____

3. What grade are you in?

   _____

4. Do you have any brothers?

   _____

5. Do you have any sisters?

   _____

7. What is your favorite color?

   _____

8. What is your favorite game?

   _____

9. What do you like best about school?

   _____

·10. Who is your best friend?

   _____

NAME _____ DATE_____

TEST

Read each group of words. Determine whether the groups are a statement, question or not a sentence. Use the code — putting the correct letter on the line following the group of words. The first one has been done for you.

Code: Statement = S
        Question = Q
        Not a Sentence = N

Put in the period or question mark where needed.

1. Mother went shopping. __S__

2. Driving in the country _____

3. What should I do with this _____

4. You should not cheat _____

5. The monkey _____

6. Who is whistling _____

7. The boy did not study for the test _____

8. Is that your brother _____

9. Our team lost the game _____

10. There is nobody at home _____

11. Where do you live _____

12. The new television show _____

13. Skating at the rink _____

14. Did you see the game _____

15. I am late for class _____

OVERVIEW

A. SENTENCE FRAGMENTS

1. **Introduction** — Write a sentence fragment on the chalkboard (e.g., This red apple). Have the students decide if it is a sentence or not. Put an ending to the sentence fragment that will make it a complete sentence — use a different color chalk.

    > e.g., This red apple *tastes good.*

    Now, put these sentence fragments on the chalkboard. Have the students complete them orally. Write the completions on the chalkboard as they give them to you. Use colored chalk for the completions. Lastly, the students should copy the complete sentences onto their papers.

    Sentence Fragments:

    a. That blue bike

    b. Slowly

    c. The sun

    d. Quietly

    e. The new boy

    f. An old car

    g. Paul and Mark are

    h. This window

2. Worksheet #154

3. Worksheet #155

4. Worksheet #156 — TEST

B. DESCRIPTIVE WORDS

1. **Introduction** — The teacher draws a small circle and a fat circle on the chalkboard. Underneath these shapes she writes descriptive phrases. Then the teacher reads each phrase that she has written and underlines the descriptive word or words in colored chalk. The teacher draws other objects (square, triangle, face, etc.) on the chalkboard and has the students describe them.

    Examples: The *small* circle

    The *tiny* circle.

The *little* circle

The *fat* circle

The *big* circle

The *large* circle

2. **Boardwork:** Write these words on the chalkboard—apple, ball, pencil, candy bar, puzzle. The students are to supply descriptive words for each object. These should be copied onto their papers.

3. Worksheet #157

4. Worksheet #158

5. Worksheet #159

6. Worksheet #160

7. **Activity**—"Which Picture?"—The teacher holds up a picture (person or animal) and describes it. She writes each descriptive phrase on the chalkboard and underlines the descriptive word(s). The students repeat each descriptive phrase upon completion. Then, the students take turns describing the remaining pictures.

   Examples: The *smiling* girl

   The *happy, little* girl

   The *big, spotted, black* dog

   The *nice* dog.

   The *playful* dog

8. **Activity**—"Guess Who?"—The teacher chooses a student to begin the game. That student whispers the name of a classmate to the teacher. Next, that student describes this classmate to the remainder of the class. The student who guesses correctly describes the next classmate.

9. Worksheet #161—TEST

C. **REVIEW—LEVEL TWO**

1. **Boardwork**—Complete each sentence by adding words or filling in the blanks.

   a. They bought a _____ car.

   b. He is a very _____ man.

   c. At eight o'clock _____.

   d. Suddenly _____.

   e. The _____ house is on fire.

   f. The _____ girl is having fun.

g. A ringing bell _____.

h. That old man _____.

2. Worksheet #162

3. Worksheet #163

NAME_____ DATE_____

Read each group of words. If the words are a complete sentence, put in the period and write *yes* on the line. If the words are not a complete sentence, write *no* on the line. The first one has been done for you.

1. Slowly the old man climbed the stairs. *yes*_____

2. Water to drink _____

3. Build a fire _____

4. The dog ran down the street _____

5. Diving into the water _____

6. This clock has stopped working _____

7. Today is the first day of winter _____

8. Running as fast as he could _____

9. Reading a story _____

10. We listened to the radio last night _____

11. The children are playing quietly _____

12. The bell is ringing _____

13. The tall building is _____

14. They bought a new house _____

15. Bill, Susan and Tom have _____

NAME_____ DATE_____

Read each group of words in COLUMN A. Match it with the correct ending in COLUMN B. Write the number of the group of words from COLUMN A on the line next to the ending it matches in COLUMN B. The first one has been done for you.

COLUMN A	COLUMN B
1. It is going	_____ is fixing my teeth.
2. That big box	__1__ to be a nice day.
3. The red ball is	_____ is too short.
4. Bob and Tom are	_____ playing baseball.
5. Mr. and Mrs. Jones live	_____ stars in the sky.
6. I am reading	_____ is filled with games.
7. The dentist	_____ beautiful, old church.
8. We went for a ride	_____ bouncing down the stairs.
9. The children went	_____ are going out to dinner.
10. Joan rides	_____ down the street.
11. This book report	_____ in the old car.
12. The sun	_____ is shining brightly.
13. There are no	_____ a very good book.
14. That is a	_____ to the park.
15. Father and Mother	_____ the bus to school.

NAME _____ DATE _____

TEST

Read each group of words. If the words are a sentence, put in the missing period. If the words are not a sentence, add words to make a complete sentence and put in the punctuation mark.

1. Suddenly

2. It is going to rain tomorrow

3. The baby is playing with the blocks

4. The young child

5. That big building

6. Quickly

7. We are going on vacation next week

8. This chair is broken

9. The boys are

10. The radio is

11. She is a good artist

12. That television program

13. Some of the girls

14. All of the candy is gone

15. I like chocolate cake

COLOR WORDS

Write the correct color word in each blank.

orange   yellow   white   red   green   black   brown   blue

1. long, _____ cucumber

2. _____ roses

3. _____ carrot sticks

4. cold, _____ snow

5. _____ tree trunk

6. _____ and _____ checkers

7. fluffy, _____ clouds

8. pretty, _____ sky

9. our _____, _____ and _____ flag

10. _____ grass

11. _____ swan

12. _____ and _____ pears

13. _____ and _____ apples

14. _____ or _____ hair

15. _____ butter

NAME_____ DATE_____

PART A: SIZE WORDS

Write an appropriate word in each blank.

small   tiny   little   big   huge   large   long   short

1. _____ winding river

2. _____ African elephant

3. _____ grey mouse

4. _____ beach ball

5. _____ stone

6. _____ rock

7. _____ man

8. _____ tree

PART B: SOUNDS WORDS

yawning   chugging   soft   tinkling   roaring   ticking

whistling   barking

1. _____ bells

2. _____ lions

3. _____ music

4. _____ wind

5. _____ train

6. _____ dogs

7. _____ baby

8. _____ clock

NAME_____ DATE_____

TASTE WORDS

Write the appropriate word in each blank.

yummy   sour   salty   sweet   tart   bitter   juicy   creamy

1. _____ honey

2. _____ lemon

3. _____ cherries

4. _____ chocolate

5. _____ dessert

6. _____ peanuts

7. _____ orange

8. _____ frosting

9. _____ cookies

10. _____ tangerine

11. _____ apple

12. _____ mashed potatoes

13. _____ cake

14. _____ pudding

15. _____ potato chips

NAME _____ DATE_____

PART A: Write a word next to each item that will describe it.

1. sandpaper_____   6. orange _____

2. puppy _____   7. music_____

3. baby chick _____   8. table _____

4. mother _____   9. cotton _____

5. chair _____   10. teacher _____

PART B: Complete each phrase by filling in the blanks before each word with appropriate descriptive words.

1. The _____, _____ man

2. A _____, _____ car

3. A _____ piece of _____ pie

4. The _____ elephant

5. That _____, _____ car

6. The _____, _____ road

7. A _____ button

8. The _____, _____ rose

9. Our _____ house

10. This _____ book

NAME _____ DATE _____

TEST

PART A: Read this short story. Underline all of the descriptive words.

John was playing with his new brown puppy. The puppy licked John's cute, round face and nibbled his freckled nose. John enjoyed playing with his small, frisky puppy. He wished for warm, sunny days so that they could run and play together.

PART B: Read this story. Fill in the blanks with appropriate words.

One dark, _____ night Dick had to walk home all alone. The wind blew through the _____ trees and made noises. The _____ moon made _____ shadows on the sidewalk. Dick broke into a _____ run. He gave a _____ sigh of relief when he saw the _____ lights in the _____ window of his home.

PART C: Write a word next to each item that will describe it.

1. swimming pool _____   6. tree _____

2. cherries _____   7. elephant _____

3. music _____   8. carrots _____

4. schoolbus _____   9. sword _____

5. clouds _____   10. cartoons _____

NAME _____ DATE_____

Write a complete sentence for each group of words. The first one has been done for you.

1. running down the road

   He saw a boy running down the road.

2. singing a song

   _____

3. at the park

   _____

4. from the living room

   _____

5. in the classroom

   _____

6. after supper

   _____

7. swimming very fast

   _____

8. eating an apple

   _____

9. the beautiful baby

   _____

10. a big dog

   _____

NAME_____ DATE_____

Read each sentence. Fill in the blanks with appropriate words.

1. I lost my _____ book.

2. That dog has a _____ coat.

3. She has _____, _____ hair.

4. This _____ cake is very good.

5. I heard a _____ scream.

6. Who broke the _____ window?

7. Have you seen my new _____ bike?

8. The _____ boys played all afternoon.

9. Dad is painting the _____ door.

10. The _____ horse is a fast runner.

11. Where is my _____ dress?

12. The _____ bells are noisy.

13. A _____ bird is in our backyard.

14. Who is that _____ lady?

15. I am in the _____ grade this year.

OVERVIEW

A. RUN-ON SENTENCES (Without Conjunctions)

1. **Introduction** — The teacher writes on the chalkboard, "What is your favorite color mine is blue." She asks the students if it is a telling sentence or an asking sentence. When the realization that it contains both a telling and an asking sentence is reached, the teacher draws a different colored line under each sentence and has a student put in the correct capital letters and punctuation marks. Then, she tells the students that capital letters and punctuation marks are signals. One of their most important signals is to tell the reader where sentences begin and end. She writes (or has already written on the chalkboard) more run-on sentences. The students read the sentences and take turns underlining the two sentences in each, as well as putting in the needed capital letters and punctuation marks.

   Examples: a. Jimmy is not here have you seen him?
                 b. My cat had three kittens we are keeping one.

2. **Boardwork** — Read each group of words. Put in the needed capital letters and periods. Do one together. Use green chalk for the beginning of the sentences so that the students know where each sentence begins.

   Sentences:
   a. the bell is ringing it is time to go in
   b. the sky is blue the sun is shining
   c. our class is giving a play our parents are coming
   d. i ran fast i won the race
   e. it is time for music we will learn a new song
   f. the wind is blowing the trees are bending
   g. he is tall his sister is taller
   h. the boys are playing tag tom is not playing

3. Worksheet #164

4. Worksheet #165

5. **Boardwork** — Copy the sentences. Put in the missing capital letters and punctuation marks.

   Sentences:
   a. Jimmy is not here have you seen him

b. My birthday is in October when is yours

c. Will you play with me we can play with my new ball

d. Would you like to play marbles I just got a new bag

e. Is the game over who won the game

f. What is in your lunch is there anything good

6. Worksheet #166

7. Worksheet #167

8. Worksheet #168

9. Worksheet #169

10. Worksheet #170 — TEST

B. **RUN-ON SENTENCES** (Using Conjunctions)

1. **Introduction** — The teacher reads a run-on sentence to the students (e.g., "We went to the park to play because it was such a pretty day and we went to see the animals, too."). After the teacher has read the sentence, she writes it on the chalkboard. Then, the teacher explains to the students what a run-on sentence is. Colored chalk is used to cross out any unneeded words and to put in the needed capital letters and punctuation marks. Once this has been completed, the teacher puts on other run-on sentences. The students take turns crossing out the unneeded words and putting in the needed capital letters and punctuation marks.

   Example: a. We went to the park to play because it was such a

   pretty day and we went to see the animals, too.

2. **Boardwork** — Write three run-on sentences on the chalkboard with conjunctions. Discuss with the students where to put in the capital letters and punctuation marks, and where to cross out the unneeded words. Students copy the sentences after discussion.

   Sentences:

   a. Mother went to the store, and then she went to the gas station and Father was at work.

   b. The boy hit a home run, so he ran around the bases and the whole team cheered for him and he was very happy.

   c. The sky got dark and I heard thunder and I saw lightning and then it began to rain so I ran into the house.

3. Worksheet #171

4. Worksheet #172

5. Worksheet #173

6. Worksheet #174 — TEST

C. **RUN-ON SENTENCES** (without and with conjunctions)

1. **Boardwork** — Read each group of words. Copy the sentences. Put in the missing capital letters and punctuation marks. Leave out the unneeded words for sentences 4, 5 and 6 (sentences d, e and f below).

Sentences:

a. it is raining what a messy day

b. how tall is Ben how tall is Linda

c. i wrote a poem will you listen to it

d. our class is taking a trip to the museum and we will see dinosaurs and we will see other interesting things, and then, we will go back to school

e. mother went to the store, and then she picked me up from school and we went to get ice cream, and then we went home

f. father plays the trumpet and mother plays the piano and Lisa plays the violin and Rick plays the drums and they have fun playing music together

2. Worksheet #175

3. Worksheet #176

4. Worksheet #177 — TEST

WRITTEN EXPRESSION

NAME_____ DATE_____

Read each group of words. There are two sentences in each group. Put in the needed capital letters and punctuation marks. The first one has been done for you.

1. There is no school today. I it is a holiday.

2. Today is Wednesday we have a ball game today.

3. This month is June next month is July.

4. It is very cloudy it is supposed to rain.

5. It is time to go home you have no homework.

6. She had a baby boy they named him Eric.

7. It is such a nice day we will have a picnic.

8. This is my math homework I don't know how to do it.

9. We went to the circus it was really fun.

10. I live in the brown house she lives in the green house.

11. My watch is not working I need to get it fixed.

12. Soon it will be time for supper we are having chicken.

13. These are my books those are yours.

14. He has a new bike it is red and white.

15. There is a new girl in our class her name is Kathy.

NAME_____ DATE_____

Read each group of words. There are two sentences in each group. Write the two sentences on the line below the group of words. Remember the capital letters and punctuation marks. The first one has been done for you.

1. today is Monday I am going to the zoo with my friends

   Today is Monday. I am going to the zoo with my friends.

2. last night it rained hard it woke me up

   _____

3. my father bought a new car it is a Ford

   _____

4. today is Mary's birthday I am going to her party

   _____

5. tomorrow is Ted's birthday he will be ten

   _____

6. the children are at the park they are flying kites

   _____

7. our family is going to Dallas we are going to fly there

   _____

8. my friend lives in Ohio she is coming to visit me

   _____

9. our class is going on a trip we are going to the museum

   _____

10. that is the last bell it is time to line up

    _____

NAME_____ DATE_____

Read each group of words. There are two sentences in each group. Put in the capital letters and punctuation marks. You will need a period and a question mark for each group. The first one has been done for you.

1. Mother made cookies. Would you like one?

2. Yesterday John was ill is he still absent today

3. He likes to play soccer is he a good player

4. Did you see that rainbow it was very pretty

5. Tomorrow is her birthday how old will she be

6. Have you seen my blue sweater I can't find it

7. Where do you live I live on Smith Street

9. Mrs. Jones had a baby was it a boy or a girl

10. I'm hungry what are we having for supper

11. I like this t.v. show may I stay up and watch all of it

12. It is time for Bill to go home where is he

13. Have you seen the new movie it is really funny

14. Did you do your chores it is time to leave for Grandma's

15. I can't find my black shoes have you seen them

NAME_____ DATE_____

Read each group of words. There are two sentences in each group. Write both sentences on the line. Put in the capital letters and punctuation marks (period and question mark).

1. this is Tueday do we have music today

   _____

2. why are you running you are to walk in the halls

   _____

3. mother baked a cake would you like some

   _____

4. how old are you i am eleven

   _____

5. we are going to the beach would you like to come with us

   _____

6. i like to play tennis do you like to play

   _____

7. mother can't find Bill have you seen him

   _____

8. where is my homework paper i can't find it

   _____

9. is that the bell i don't want to go in yet

   _____

10. do you think it will snow it is getting colder

NAME_____ DATE_____

Read each group of words. Put in the missing capital letters and punctuation marks.
Some of the groups are two sentences.

1. Jack joined the football team in September

2. have you seen my shoes they are brown ones

3. bill caught a large fish jack caught two small ones

4. the picnic will be at Cooper Park

5. where did you put that library book

6. where is the ball game is it at Washington Park

7. wow, what a catch Bill is a great baseball player

8. today is my birthday are you coming to my party

9. did you see the play

10. that is a pretty house

11. does Nick have his report finished

12. this is my bike where is yours

13. what is your name where do you live

14. there is no school today it is Saturday

15. what a great play our team should win the game

NAME_____ DATE_____

PART A   Read the paragraph. Put in the needed capital letters and punctuation marks, so that the paragraph will not have run-on sentences. Now have your teacher check the paragraph.

We went to Hawaii at Christmas we flew over on a jet plane and came back by boat

Mother liked the plane ride best my dad and I liked the boat ride we had lots of fun in

Hawaii.

PART B   After your teacher has checked PART A, write the story on these lines with the correct capital letters and punctuation marks.

_____

_____

_____

_____

_____

_____

_____

_____

_____

_____

_____

_____

WRITTEN EXPRESSION

NAME _____ DATE_____

TEST

Read each group of words. On the line after the group, tell if the group of words is a statement, question, or run-on sentence. Then put in the needed capital letters and punctuation marks. The first one has been done for you.

1. What time is the movie? *question* _____

2. it is raining hard the sky is dark _____

3. yesterday was a sunny day _____

4. are you going to the party it should be fun _____

5. christmas is a holiday _____

6. we are having hamburgers for supper doesn't that sound good _____

7. whose book is this _____

8. school will soon be out for the summer _____

9. see the rainbow in the sky isn't it pretty _____

10. bob is the pitcher tom is the catcher _____

11. our family is taking a trip to Disneyland have you ever been there_____

12. mrs. Jones is a nice lady _____

13. will you help me rake the yard_____

14. our class is having a kick ball game will you come and watch _____

15. where is the movie what time is the movie _____

NAME _____ DATE_____

Read each group of words. Take out the unneeded words. Put in the needed capital letters and punctuation marks.

1. The sun is shining and the sky is clear so we are going on a picnic.

2. She went to see a movie, and then she went to the ice cream shop, and then she went home.

3. We will have art today because it is wednesday and we are going to paint today, so I am happy.

4. Mother made a chocolate cake and Father bought some ice cream and we had both for dessert.

5. Our team is in first place because we have not lost any games yet and I hope we do not lose any at all.

6. Mother took me shopping because I need some new clothes because I have grown too big for my old clothes.

7. We have sold our house and we have bought a bigger house and I will have my own bedroom and I am really happy about that.

8. I like to play soccer but my brother likes to play baseball and my friend likes to play football but we all like to ride bikes together and play basketball.

NAME_____ DATE_____

PART A   Read the paragraph. Cross out the unneeded words. Put in the needed capital letters and punctuation marks. Have your teacher check this part when you are finished.

It was raining so we had to stay inside and so we played games such as Monopoly, Checkers, Hide and Seek, and Old Maid, and then Mother made us some popcorn and we ate it while we watched television, and then we helped Mother make supper for Dad and us.

PART B   Now write the paragraph on these lines with the correct capital letters and punctuation marks.

_____

_____

_____

_____

_____

_____

_____

_____

_____

_____

_____

NAME _____ DATE_____

Read each group of words. Cross out the unneeded words. Write the sentences on the lines with the correct capital letters and punctuation marks.

1. it is almost time to go home so we must line up and we will leave when the bell rings _____

    _____

2. there is no math today because we have an assembly and Tom is happy _____

    _____

3. he was a ghost for Halloween and his sister was a princess and his little brother was a cowboy _____

    _____

4. yesterday it snowed all day so we made a snowman today and then we had a snowball fight _____

    _____

5. our family is going on vacation out East and we are going by car and we will go to Boston and then we will go to New York City and then we will go to Philadelphia and then we will go down to Washington, D.C. and we will see and do many things on our trip _____

    _____

    _____

    _____

6. there is no school today because it is Thanksgiving so we are going to our grandmother's house for dinner and we will have turkey to eat and then we will play games and have a very nice day _____

    _____

    _____

    _____

NAME_____ DATE_____

TEST

Read each group of words. On the line after the group, tell if the group of words is a statement, question, or run-on sentence. Then put in the needed capital letters and punctuation marks. Also, cross out any unneeded words in the run-on sentences. The first one has been done for you.

1. Mother and Father have gone to a dinner party. *statement* _____

2. she is writing a report her report is on dogs _____

3. where did you put your tennis racket _____

4. after school Tom is going to ride his bike, and then he is going to go over to Bob's house, and then they are going to the park to play ball. _____

5. what is on television i want to watch something funny_____

6. the black car drove quickly down our street _____

7. what street do you live on what color is your house _____

8. will you pick me up after school, please _____

9. we are going to the beach today because it is so hot and we will go swimming there, and then we will play in the sand and for lunch we will have hot dogs, and then we will come home _____

_____

_____

_____

10. the wind is blowing very hard _____

11. where are my books what did I do with them _____

12. the boys are playing tag the girls are jumping rope _____

NAME_____ DATE_____

PART A   Read the paragraph. Put in the missing punctuation marks. Have your teacher check PART A when you are finished.

My scout troop is going on a camp-out this week-end we will be gone for two days we will sleep in the woods for one night it will be fun to sleep in a tent we will cook our own food we will learn many things about the woods this week-end it's going to be a great week-end

PART B   Now write the paragraph on these lines putting in the correct capital letters and punctuation marks.

_____

_____

_____

_____

_____

_____

_____

_____

_____

_____

_____

_____

NAME_____ DATE_____

PART A Read the paragraph. Cross out the extra words. Put in the missing capital letters and punctuation marks. Have your teacher check PART A when you are finished.

mary likes to play the piano so she practices for one hour each day and she played for our class today because we wanted to hear her and she played three songs and they were all hard and she did an excellent job and we wished we could play the piano like her

PART B Now write the paragraph on these lines with the correct capital letters and punctuation marks.

_____

_____

_____

_____

_____

_____

_____

_____

_____

_____

_____

_____

NAME_____ DATE_____

TEST

Read each group of words. Put in the needed capital letters and punctuation marks. Some of the run-on sentences have extra words which should be crossed out.

1. scott went to see the Yankees play ball

2. the team practiced very hard for the game, and then they cleaned up, and then they went home for supper

3. have you gone to see the new play

4. they are going to the high school concert

5. susan is a new girl at our school we are going to invite her to our party we hope that she will make new friends and that she will have fun at the party

6. the moon is shining there are stars in the sky

7. it will soon be time for the baby to go to bed

8. i have a horse i ride my horse every day

9. pat bought a skirt and blouse at the store

10. would you please get some wood for the fireplace

11. my brother has gone to football camp it is in Michigan

12. the girls went to see a movie, and then they went to eat, and then they went shopping, and then they went home

13. how far is it to the restaurant i'm very hungry

14. does Cheryl like to read mysteries

15. there is going to be a scary movie on television tonight

OVERVIEW

A. COMBINING SHORT SENTENCES INTO ONE COMPLEX SENTENCE

1. **Introduction** – Two tagboard trains are put one behind the other along the chalkboard ledge.

> The teacher says: "The railroad does not send two short trains to the same destination. They put all the cars behind one engine making one long train."

The teacher removes the first caboose and the second engine to make one long train.

> The teacher then says: "When we write sentences, we often combine two short sentences to make one long sentence."

The teacher reverses the boxcars to show the sentence, "I like cake," and the other boxcars to reveal the sentence, "I don't like spinach." An engine pulls each train. Have a student read each sentence.

> Next, the teacher says: "By removing the period at the end of the first sentence (the teacher removes the caboose) and adding the word *but* (the teacher replaces the second engine with the boxcar that has the word *but* on it), we can combine two short sentences into one long sentence." A student then reads the new sentence.

The teacher explains that some words that can be used to combine sentences include *but, and, so,* etc. She uses the same technique for the following sentences explaining that sometimes we remove more than one word as in sentence one below: "I like to ride a bike and roller skate."

> 1. I like to ride a bike.   I like to roller skate.

2. **Boardwork:** Copy these sentences onto your paper. Make the two sentences into one long sentence by adding a word or words. Do not change the word order of the sentences.

Sentences:

a. It is raining. The sun is shining.

b. There is no school today. It is a holiday.

c. Our teacher is absent. She is sick.

d. Two boys are absent. Four girls are absent.

e. I saw several stars in the sky. They looked like a tiger.

f. I bought a puzzle. My friend bought a game.

g. We are going ice skating. We will have fun.

h. Carl won first prize. Brad won second prize.

3. Worksheet #178

4. **Boardwork** — Copy these sentences onto your papers. Make the two sentences into one long sentence by adding a word or words. You may take out the extra words. We will do one together.

Sentences:

Example: I like to ride my bike. I like to run in races. I like to ride my bike and run in races.

a. Father is going out to eat. Mother is going with him.

b. The boy is walking to school. The girl is walking to school.

c. Sam has a new baseball. Sam has an old glove.

d. The girls went to the park. Their dogs went with them.

e. Nancy likes peas. She doesn't like beans.

f. Have you seen Tim? Have you seen Scott?

g. I saw Brenda at the zoo. I saw Carol at the park.

5. Worksheet #179

6. **Activity** — "Practice" — Each student writes two short sentences that can and should be combined on his paper. (The teacher should check these sentences.) The students then exchange papers and combine the short sentences on that paper into one long sentence.

7. Worksheet #180 — TEST

B. SUBJECT - VERB AGREEMENT

1. **Introduction** — The teacher writes two sentences on the chalkboard: "She is a nice girl," and "She are a nice girl." These sentences are read by the teacher. She asks the students which sentence sounds correct. Once they tell her the correct sentence, she erases the other sentence from the board. Last, the teacher writes other pairs of sentences on the chalkboard. She explains to the students that the subject and the verb of the sentence have to agree for the sentence to be correct. Students take turns reading the pairs of sentences and determining which sentence is correct. Then, they come to the board and erase the incorrect sentence from the board. The students are instructed to copy all of the correct sentences from the board onto their papers.

Sentences:

a. They gone to the park.
    They went to the park.

b. I have a new bike.
    He have a new bike.

  c. We is going to see grandmother.
   We are going to see grandmother.

  d. Mother make a cake.
   Mother made a cake.

  e. Father paint the house.
   Father painted the house.

  f. Will you come to my party?
   Will you came to my party?

2. Worksheet #181

3. **Boardwork**—Write pairs of sentences on the chalkboard. Students are to choose the correct sentence for each pair, and then write the correct sentences on their papers.

  a. I am going to the zoo with my family.
   I are going to the zoo with my family.

  b. Father come home late from work.
   Father came home late from work.

  c. He is playing basketball at the gym.
   I are playing basketball at the gym.

  d. Where did you put your notebook?
   Where does you put your notebook?

  e. Were Todd at the game?
   Was Todd at the game?

  f. Are the children at the park?
   Is the children at the park?

4. Worksheet #182

5. **Boardwork**—Explain to the students that when a sentence has a plural subject (naming two people), it needs a plural verb. Read each sentence and discuss this concept with them. Students are to copy the sentences onto their papers.

  Sentences:

  a. Mother and I *are* going to the store.

  b. Paul and Tom *were* at the ball game.

  c. Father and Mother *love* me.

  d. Ken and Kathy *drink* milk every day.

  e. The boy and girl *walk* to school.

  f. Father and I *like* to go fishing.

6. Worksheet #183

7. Worksheet #184—TEST

C. **REVIEW** (Level Four Skills)

1. **Boardwork** — Read each pair of sentences. Make the sentences into one sentence. Write this sentence on your paper.

    Sentences:

    a. Tom is playing basketball. George is playing, too.

    b. I like to read books. I like to listen to music.

    c. Jean is going to Dallas. Laura is going with her.

    d. Mother went to the store. Ruth went along for the ride.

    e. Bob likes math. He doesn't like spelling.

    f. Where does Jim live? Where does Ted live?

    g. There is no music today. The music teacher is not here.

    h. Father is painting the garage door. Sam is helping him.

2. **Activity** — Review "Practice" Activity from Section A of this level.

3. Worksheet #185 — REVIEW TEST

4. **Boardwork** — Read each sentence. Copy the sentence with the correct word in it chosen from the pair of words in the parentheses.

    Sentences:

    a. She (have, has) a big smile on her face.

    b. I (saw, seen) the movie yesterday.

    c. (He, I) knows what to do.

    d. Does the baby know how to (walk, walks)?

    e. That boy (eat, eats) too fast.

    f. Susan and Karen (is, are) going home now.

    g. (I, Bob) am not feeling well.

    h. (They, Ted) runs very quickly.

5. Worksheet #186

6. Worksheet #187

7. Worksheet #188 — REVIEW TEST

D. **REVIEW — ALL WRITTEN EXPRESSION SKILLS**

1. **Boardwork** — Write sentences on the chalkboard. Students are to copy the sentences and then are to put in the ending punctuation mark (period, question mark, exclamation point).

Sentences:

a. Where is your lunch

b. This is a pretty day

c. We won the game

d. Have you seen my math book

e. I lost my blue pencil

f. I feel miserable

g. What time is the party

h. Here are your keys

2. Worksheet #189

3. Worksheet #190

4. **REVIEW** any games and activities from all of the WRITTEN EXPRESSION Levels.

5. **Boardwork**—Complete each sentence by adding words or by filling in the blanks.

Sentences:

a. The tall man _____.

b. We live in a _____ house.

c. This _____ cake tastes good.

d. Quickly _____.

e. On Wednesday _____.

f. She bought a _____ dress.

g. Our television _____.

h. They live on a _____ street.

6. Worksheet #191

7. Worksheet #192

8. **Boardwork**—Read the sentences. Copy the sentences putting in the missing capital letters and punctuation marks. Leave out the unneeded words for sentences 4, 5, 6 (d, e, f below).

Sentences:

a. i finished my report will you read it

b. there is no school today it is Christmas

c. who lives on South Street who lives on State Avenue

d. it is raining and we have to walk home and we don't have our coats or umbrellas so we will get wet

e. there is going to be a party at Jim's house for Tony his birthday is next week he will be gone then so the party is going to be this week

f. I am going shopping because I need to get a new dress because I am going to Tony's birthday party and because I need to get him a gift.

9. Worksheet #193

10. **Boardwork** — Read each pair of sentences. Make the pair into one sentence. Write this sentence on your paper.

   Sentences:
   a. Paul is flying to Denver. He is going to visit his grandparents.

   b. Mother is fixing supper. Sue is helping her.

   c. Have you met Tim? Have you met Ben?

   d. There is no ball game today. The field is too wet.

   e. Mike finished his math. He didn't finish his science.

   f. Fay went to the store. She went to the library, too.

11. Worksheet #194

12. **Boardwork** — Write a sentence on your paper for each of these words.
   a. are
   b. eat
   c. Mike and Todd
   d. Kim and Ann
   e. was
   f. went
   g. break
   h. am

13. Worksheet #195

14. Worksheet #196

NAME_____ DATE_____

Read each set of sentences. Put these sentences together into one long sentence. You may add a word or words, but do not change the order of the words in either sentence. Write the long sentences on the lines. The first one has been done for you.

1. I am going to the dentist. I can't stay for music today.

   I am going to the dentist, so I can't stay for music today.

2. It is raining. A lot of the snow is melting.

   _____

3. I am going to see a movie. I need to go to the store first.

   _____

4. It is Tim's birthday. He is going to have a party.

   _____

5. Our cat had three kittens. We kept one of them.

   _____

6. It is getting colder. Soon it will start to snow.

   _____

7. I have to do a report. I need to go to the library.

   _____

8. His bike is green. His sister's is yellow.

   _____

9. I am not going to school today. I have a fever.

   _____

10. Mother has gone to the library. Father is at work.

   _____

NAME_____ DATE_____

Read each set of sentences. Make the two sentences into one sentence by adding a word or words. You may cross out the extra words. Write the sentences on the lines. Example: Bill likes to play ball. He likes to play soccer. Bill likes to play ball and soccer.

1. Father is painting the garage. He is painting the shed, too.

   _____

2. Mr. Young's class is going to see a film. Miss Smith's class is going to see the film, too.

   _____

3. I like to read books. I like to play the piano.

   _____

4. Susan likes math class. She likes gym class.

   _____

5. Father is going fishing. Ted is going with him.

   _____

6. Mother is going shopping. She took Sarah and Ruth with her.

   _____

7. Mr. Jackson went to the dinner party. His wife will meet him there.

   _____

8. I am doing a hard puzzle. My brother is helping me.

   _____

9. Tom is studying for the spelling test. Jim is studying with him.

   _____

10. I am going to the beach. Lisa is going with me.

   _____

NAME_____ DATE_____

TEST

Read each set of sentences. Put the sentences together into one sentence. You may add a word or words. Write your sentences on the lines.

1. There is no picnic today. It is raining hard.

   _____

2. How old is Beth? How old is Karen?

   _____

3. John is building a tree house. Carl is helping him.

   _____

4. Susan went to see a play. Patricia went with her.

   _____

5. I am writing a report on Africa. Mary is helping me.

   _____

6. There is no art today. The art teacher is sick.

   _____

7. Mark likes to draw horses. He likes to draw animals, too.

   _____

8. It is very cold. We will stay inside today.

   _____

9. There is no school tomorrow. It is Saturday.

   _____

10. Did John finish his math? Did Brian finish his math?

   _____

NAME_____ DATE_____

Read each pair of sentences. Underline the correct sentence for each pair. The first one has been done for you.

1. I are going to the party.
    <u>I am going to the party.</u>

2. Did you watch all of the television show?
    Did you watches all of the television show?

3. Who blew the whistle?
    Who blowed the whistle?

4. Our class is going to sing in the program.
    Our class is going to sang in the program.

5. The girls wants to see a movie.
    The girls want to see a movie.

6. Mark drawn a picture of an eagle.
    Mark drew a picture of an eagle.

7. We are going to flies to Los Angeles.
    We are going to fly to Los Angeles.

8. Did you brings the cookies?
    Did you bring the cookies?

9. The boys like to play catch.
    The boys likes to play catch.

10. I saw Paula at the park.
    I seen Paula at the park.

11. Tom threw the ball far.
    Tom thrown the ball far.

12. Mother love me very much.
    Mother loves me very much.

13. Our teacher smile a lot.
    Our teacher smiles a lot.

14. He eaten the whole thing.
    He ate the whole thing.

15. How fast can you runs?
    How fast can you run?

NAME_____ DATE_____

Write a sentence for each word or words.

1. they

_____

2. the men

_____

3. gone

_____

4. looks

_____

5. everyone

_____

6. takes

_____

7. the children

_____

8. smiled

_____

9. plays

_____

10. George

_____

11. brings

_____

12. Betty

_____

NAME _____ DATE_____

Read each sentence. Circle the word in the parentheses that will complete the sentence correctly.

1. Did Mark and John (plays, play) ball on Friday?

2. Father and Mother (work, works) downtown.

3. The big boy and the little boy (like, likes) to ride bikes each day.

4. The cat and dog (is, are) chasing each other.

5. Mother and I (love, loves) to bake goodies.

6. Jean and Sally (has, have) gone to the library.

7. The twins (runs, run) very fast in all the races.

8. Both Karen and Tim (loves, love) their little baby brother.

9. Father and I (throws, throw) the ball after supper each day.

10. Bill and Jane (was, were) at the dance last night.

11. Did Jill and Carla (takes, take) their lunch to school today?

12. Bob and Sarah (flies, fly) home each Christmas.

13. Did Carl and Ted (seen, see) the car accident?

14. Father and Mother (want, wants) to get a new car.

15. (Has, Have) John and Dave found the path?

NAME_____ DATE_____

TEST

Read each sentence. Fill in the blank with a word that will complete each sentence.

1. Where _____ the children playing?

2. We _____ to school each day.

3. Bill and Ken_____ to the soccer game.

4. They _____ watching the fireworks.

5. _____ is not at school today.

6. _____ drinks a lot of water each day.

7. The boys _____ hard on building the treehouse.

8. The girls _____ gone to the store.

9. Have _____ and _____ come home yet?

10. Did _____ wear her new dress today?

11. Nancy and Laura _____ lunch at home everyday.

12. Bob _____ a new baseball glove.

13. Who has _____ the window?

14. _____ draws very well.

15. The baby _____ often.

NAME_____ DATE_____

REVIEW TEST

Read each set of sentences. Put the sentences together into one sentence. You may add a word or words, if needed; or you may remove words, if needed. Write your sentences on the lines.

1. We had to leave the park. It started to rain.

   _____

2. There is no school today. It is snowing too hard.

   _____

3. Susan likes to draw. She likes to paint, too.

   _____

4. Carl has left for the game. Ted has already left.

   _____

5. Mother went to the health club. Father is going to meet her there.

   _____

6. Where are my gloves? Where is my hat?

   _____

7. We are going out to dinner. We will see a play, too.

   _____

8. Today is Labor Day. We are having a family picnic.

   _____

9. I like to listen to music. I like to read mysteries.

   _____

10. Bill likes to play tennis. He doesn't like to play golf.

   _____

NAME_____ DATE_____

Write a sentence for each word.

1. is

_____

2. are

_____

3. am

_____

4. was

_____

5. were

_____

6. eats

_____

7. like

_____

8. wants

_____

9. go

_____

10. smiles

_____

11. take

_____

12. draws

_____

NAME _____ DATE_____

Read each sentence. There is something incorrect in each sentence. Cross out the incorrect word in each sentence. Write the correct word for each sentence on the line following it.

1. I doesn't have any more pencils. _____

2. He sing very well. _____

3. She walk home slowly every day. _____

4. They is going out to eat. _____

5. I seen the accident happen. _____

6. Do you loves your parents? _____

7. How far can he throws the ball? _____

8. Tom go to ball practice today. _____

9. Are there school tomorrow? _____

10. Kim and Jill was at the party. _____

11. Ted seen them there. _____

12. Mary want to go with you. _____

13. Father and Mother is at the gym. _____

14. Who drawn this picture? _____

15. Keith and Mark will bring the baseballs and bats. _____

NAME_____ DATE_____

REVIEW TEST

Read each sentence. Circle the word in the parentheses that will make each sentence correct.

1. Bob (run, runs) very fast.

2. I (saw, seen) the race.

3. I think Bob will (wins, win) the race.

4. The men (is, are) at work.

5. The women (were, was) at the store.

6. Paul and John (lives, live) next door.

7. Father and Mother (is, are) at the picnic.

8. Their children (goed, went) with them.

9. Our dog (eat, eats) a lot.

10. Who (drawn, drew) this picture?

11. Nancy and Carol (have, has) gone to the museum.

12. Did Mark (plays, play) in the game?

13. Mr. and Mrs. Cooper have (flew, flown) to New York.

14. Bill (are, is) not here now.

15. Did Bill (goes, go) to the park already?

NAME_____ DATE_____

Read each sentence. Put in the period, question mark, or exclamation point at the end of each sentence.

1. Today is Christmas

2. May we go see the fireworks

3. It is starting to snow

4. Bill has a new bike

5. Did you see Carol at school today

6. That store is on fire

7. Look out for that falling tree

8. We are going on vacation

9. Will you help me with my report

10. I didn't study for the test

11. Mr. and Mrs. Lewis are moving into a new home

12. What a pretty day this is

13. How much does this cost

14. Debby bought a new dress

15. Who won the game

NAME_____ DATE_____

PART A: Write a sentence for each word.

1. teacher

   _____

2. love

   _____

3. house

   _____

4. is

   _____

5. came

   _____

PART B: Write a sentence beginning with each word.

6. How

   _____

7. Where

   _____

8. Who

   _____

9. Did

   _____

10. Are

   _____

NAME_____ DATE_____

Read each group of words. If the words are a sentence, put in the period. If the words are not a sentence, add words to make a complete sentence and put in the period.

1. Someone is

2. There are no cookies left

3. That noisy boy

4. All of the pencils

5. Suddenly

6. This tiny bird

7. This is my baby brother

8. One of the children

9. The ringing bell

10. This is my last math problem

11. On Friday

12. Our class is going on a picnic

13. The threatening clouds

14. The radio is broken

15. A big dog

NAME _____ DATE_____

PART A: Write a word next to each item that will describe it.

1. plate _____   6. mother _____

2. flowers _____   7. bird _____

3. sky _____   8. kitten _____

4. apple _____   9. hamburger _____

5. father _____   10. grass _____

PART B: Complete each sentence with a word or words that will make sense.

1. Mother bought _____ and _____ grapes at the store.

2. We lost our _____ beach ball.

3. The _____ elephant was fun to watch.

4. I will be in _____ grade next year.

5. The _____, _____ car belongs to us.

6. I had a _____ piece of _____ cake for a snack.

7. She is missing _____ buttons off her blouse.

8. Kevin lost his _____ book.

9. The _____, _____ roses were a gift for me.

10. The _____, _____ chick can hardly move.

NAME_____ DATE_____

PART A: Read each group of words. Put in the missing capital letters and punctuation marks.

1. i got a new puppy i play with him all the time.

2. they have gone on vacation they went to Texas

3. there will be no school tomorrow it is Thanksgiving

4. did you mow the lawn did you pull the weeds

5. this is my sister her name is Beth

6. on Thursday we are going on a trip we are going to a farm

7. do you like to play Monopoly i like to play cards

8. bill has a new friend his name is Mark

9. sally went to see her friend she lives in California

10. the bell is ringing it is a fire drill

PART B: Read each group of words. Cross out the extra words. Put in the missing
capital letters and punctuation marks.

1. Ben and Jack are playing inside today because it is raining and they are unhappy
because they were supposed to go swimming at John's house

2. I think it is going to be a pretty day because the sun is already shining and the sky
has no clouds in it and the birds are singing so I feel happy

3. Last summer we flew to California for our vacation and we went to Disneyland
first and then we went to the beach and then we drove to the mountains and we
had a lot of fun and we didn't want to come home.

4. Today is our math test and I didn't study for it because I forgot and I am really
scared about it but I have nobody to blame but myself

NAME_____ DATE_____

Read each set of sentences. Put the sentences together into one sentence. You may add a word or words, if needed; or you may remove words, if needed. Write your sentences on the lines.

1. Father is working in the garden. Mother is helping him.

   _____

2. The boy lost his hat. The boy lost his mittens.

   _____

3. I bought a new dress. I, also, bought some shoes.

   _____

4. There will be a parade tomorrow. It will be Memorial Day.

   _____

5. Did you make your bed? Did you clean the bathroom?

   _____

6. We are having a dinner party. It is our parents' anniversary.

   _____

7. It is such a nice day. Our family is going for a drive.

   _____

8. Are there any chips left? Are there any cherries left?

   _____

9. Robin likes to ride bikes. She likes to jog, too.

   _____

10. We have a pet dog. We have a cat, too.

   _____

11. Where does Ben live? Where does Ken live?

   _____

NAME_____ DATE_____

Read each sentence. Circle the word in the parentheses that will complete each sentence.

1. Father and Tim (seen, saw) an alligator.

2. My parents (love, loves) me.

3. Did you (bring, brings) your jacket with you?

4. Who (took, taken) the pictures?

5. (He, I) has eaten dinner.

6. The girl (doesn't, don't) want any juice.

7. Beth and Joy (want, wants) to come to the party.

8. May they (come, came)?

9. How many times has Dad (flew, flown)?

10. (I, She) smile all the time.

11. I (doesn't, don't) know what to do with this.

12. Mother has (went, gone) shopping.

13. The men (are, is) playing ball.

14. The women (is, are) playing ball, too.

15. Joe and Gary (were, was) at the park this afternoon.

NAME_____ DATE_____

Read each sentence. Cross out the incorrect word. Write the correct word for each sentence on the line following it.

1. Don't Ben know where the game is? _____

2. The baby smile a lot._____

3. Beth are at the zoo. _____

4. The girls is with her. _____

5. Who runned in the race? _____

6. Did you seen that error? _____

7. Ken and Gary will help moves the furniture._____

8. They isn't at home now. _____

9. I works hard every day. _____

10. Mr. Brown go home at four o'clock. _____

11. The wind has blew hard today. _____

12. She like to dance. _____

13. I is not feeling well. _____

14. The big dog and the little dog chases the mailman. _____

15. What did you brings me for lunch?_____